CALIFORNIA

Interactive Reading Notepad: Inquiry Companion

WORLD HISTORY
THE MODERN WORLD

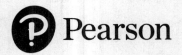
Pearson

Acknowledgments

Grateful acknowledgment is made to the following for copyrighted material:

Images:
Cover: Tower Bridge, London, United Kingdom. Andrew Marriott/Moment/Getty Images

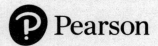

ISBN-13: 978-1-41-828673-6
ISBN-10:   1-41-828673-7

Contents

California World History: The Modern World
Interactive Reading Notepad: Inquiry Companion

Absolutism and Revolution

Lesson 1 Absolute Monarchy in Spain and France

Key Terms

absolute monarchy	Henry IV
divine right	Edict of Nantes
Hapsburg empire	Cardinal Richelieu
Charles V	Louis XIV
Philip II	intendant
armada	Jean-Baptiste Colbert
El Greco	Versailles
Miguel de Cervantes	*levée*
Huguenots	balance of power

Academic Vocabulary

cumbersome: hard to handle because of size, weight, or many parts

erode: wear away or disintegrate

Lesson Objectives

1 **Identify** the characteristics of absolute monarchy, including the concept of divine right.

2 **Explain** how Spanish power grew under Charles V and Philip II.

3 **Understand** how France built a centralized monarchy after the wars of religion.

4 **Evaluate** Louis XIV as an absolute monarch.

5 **Describe** how the arts flourished in Spain and France.

Ruling with Absolute Power: Text

1. **Explain an Argument** If Louis XIV truly ruled by divine right, what risk did his subjects run if they questioned his authority?

Spain and the Hapsburg Empire: Text

2. **Summarize** What role did religion play in the policies of Charles V?

3. **Draw Inferences** How did foreign conflict play a role in Charles V's abdication of the throne?

Philip II Becomes an Absolute Monarch: Text

4. **Identify Cause and Effect** Why did Philip try to invade England? What was the result?

5. **Drawing Conclusions** Reread the text "Battles in the Mediterranean and the Netherlands." Why do you think Spain joined with Venice and other Italian states in the Battle of Lepanto?

6. **Using Visual Information** Look at the map of the Wars of Philip II. Which battles shown took place in territory ruled directly by Spain?

7. **Drawing Inferences** What decisions did Spanish rulers make that weakened Spain's economy?

Arts and Literature of Spain's Golden Century: Text

8. **Draw Conclusions** What is one reason the arts might have flourished during this period of Spanish history?

Royal Power Expands in France: Text

9. **Determine Author's Point of View** What do you think Henry IV meant when he said, "Paris is well worth a Mass"?

10. **Identify Cause and Effect** How did Richelieu's treatment of the nobles and the Huguenots strengthen the monarchy?

Louis XIV, an Absolute Monarch: Text

11. Determine Author's Point of View Louis XIV called himself the "Sun King" and said, "I am the State." Describe how each statement reflects absolutism, and explain which you find to be the best "slogan" for Louis XIV.

12. Use Visual Information Study the infographic on Louis XIV and absolutism. What does it take to be a successful absolute monarch?

The Royal Palace at Versailles: Text

13. Cite Evidence How did Louis control the nobles? Use examples from the text.

The Legacy of Louis XIV: Text

14. Identify Cause and Effect What are some possible effects (both foreign and domestic) from Louis XIV's many costly wars?

15. Analyze Interactions Why did Louis XIV expel the Huguenots? In your opinion, was it a good decision or a bad decision? Why?

Absolutism and Revolution

Lesson 2 Rise of Austria, Prussia, and Russia

Key Terms

elector	Peter the Great
mercenary	westernization
depopulation	boyar
Peace of Westphalia	autocratic
Maria Theresa	warm-water port
War of the Austrian Succession	St. Petersburg
Prussia	Catherine the Great
Frederick William I	partition
Frederick II	

Academic Vocabulary

aspired: aim; sought

stipulated: made a specific demand

Lesson Objectives

1 **Outline** the causes and results of the Thirty Years' War.

2 **Understand** how Austria and Prussia emerged as great powers.

3 **Explain** the steps Peter the Great took to modernize Russia.

4 **Describe** how Russia grew under Peter the Great and Catherine the Great.

5 **Describe** how European nations tried to maintain a balance of power.

The Thirty Years' War: Text

1. **Use Visual Information** Look at the map of "Europe After the Thirty Years War". Which regions in the Holy Roman Empire were mainly Catholic?

2. **Compare and Contrast** Compare the maps of the Holy Roman Empire before the Thirty Years' War and of Europe after the war. Which two states came into existence after the 30 Years' War? What else do these two states have in common?

Hapsburg Austria Expands: Text

3. **Draw Inferences** What kinds of conflicts could emerge in an empire as diverse as the Hapsburg Empire?

4. **Draw Conclusions** What might have motivated Maria Theresa to reform tax policies?

Prussia Emerges: Text

5. **Cite Evidence** How did Frederick William I gain the loyalty of the Prussian nobles? Can you think of two other methods that absolutist rulers have used to control their nobility? Which were most successful? Why?

6. **Paraphrase** What does the phrase "Prussia is not a state which possesses an army, but an army which possesses a state" mean? What does this say about Prussia's values?

Peter the Great Modernizes Russia: Text

7. **Drawing Inferences** Peter the Great's motto was "I am a student and I seek teachers." How do you think this motto relates to his practice of observing everyday people when he toured Western cities?

8. **Cite Evidence** How did Peter the Great westernize Russia? Cite at least three examples.

Expanding Russia's Borders: Text

9. **Drawing Inferences** What is one reason that Peter the Great greatly expanded the military during this reign?

Catherine the Great: Text

10. **Compare and Contrast** How were Catherine the Great's goals similar to those of Peter? How did they differ?

11. **Categorize** Catherine the Great continued Peter the Great's efforts to westernize Russia and was also a ruthless leader like her predecessors. Give examples of both her reforms and her repression in a paragraph in which you assess Catherine's strength as a leader.

12. **Using Visual Information** Look at the map of Russia's Expansion, 1689– 1796. Why were the ports on the Black Sea more appealing to Russia than those in Asia?

Five Great European Powers: Text

13. **Determine Central Ideas** In the 16th and 17th centuries, alliances between countries were formed based on religion. In the 18th century, what were these alliances based on? What does this say about trends within European politics?

Absolutism and Revolution

Lesson 3 Triumph of Parliament in England

Key Terms

James I	limited monarchy
dissenter	constitutional government
Puritan	cabinet
Charles I	prime minister
Oliver Cromwell	oligarchy
English Bill of Rights	

Academic Vocabulary

suppressed: kept from being revealed; put down by force

justification: the state of having shown to be just, right, or reasonable

tolerate: to respect others beliefs without sharing them

Lesson Objectives

1 **Describe** the Tudor monarchs' relations with Parliament.

2 **Analyze** how clashes between the Stuarts and Parliament ushered in a century of revolution.

3 **Understand** how the English Civil War and the development of the Commonwealth led to the Glorious Revolution.

4 **Explain** the development of English constitutional government.

Tudor Monarchs Work with Parliament: Text

1. **Cite Evidence** How did Elizabeth I handle her relationship with Parliament? Why do you think this was the case? Cite evidence from the text in your answer.

Stuart Monarchs Clash with Parliament: Text

2. **Compare and Contrast** How was James I similar to and different from Elizabeth I?

3. **Analyze Interactions** Why did Parliament react so negatively to James I's speech about divine right?

4. **Identify Cause and Effect** How are the Long Parliament and the imposition of the Anglican prayer book connected?

The English Civil War: Text

5. **Analyze Sequence** Use this graphic organizer to help you take notes about the sequence of events leading up to the English Civil War.

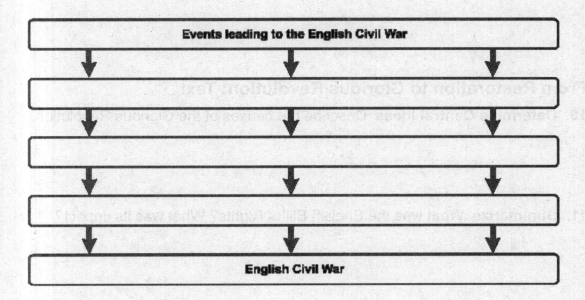

6. **Identify Supporting Details** What are some reasons for the Roundhead victory?

7. **Draw Inferences** Why did European monarchs respond as they did to the death of Charles I?

Cromwell and the Commonwealth: Text

8. **Summarize** What happened in Ireland during the Commonwealth period, and why?

Interactive Reading Notepad • Lesson 3

9. **Compare Authors' Points of View** Compare the points of view of the Leveller quote in this Reading with James I's statement about divine right in the Reading "Stuart Monarchs Clash with Parliament." How do these two statements reflect different ideas about the rights of human beings?

From Restoration to Glorious Revolution: Text

10. **Determine Central Ideas** Describe the causes of the Glorious Revolution.

11. **Summarize** What was the English Bill of Rights? What was its impact?

England's Constitutional Government Evolves: Text

12. **Compare and Contrast** Describe the differences between the Tories and the Whigs.

13. **Identify Supporting Details** What was the makeup of George I's cabinet? What purpose did they serve?

14. **Use Visual Information** How does this image of the marketplace show the class divisions in England in the 1700s?

Absolutism and Revolution

Lesson 4 The Enlightenment

Key Terms

natural law

Thomas Hobbes

John Locke

social contract

natural right

philosophe

Montesquieu

Voltaire

Jean-Jacques Rousseau

laissez faire

Adam Smith

free market

free enterprise system

censorship

salons

baroque

rococo

enlightened despot

Joseph II

Academic Vocabulary

philosophy: love of, or the search for, wisdom or knowledge

evolved: developed gradually over time

Lesson Objectives

1 **Describe** how science led to the Enlightenment.

2 **Explain** the political philosophies of Hobbes, Locke, Voltaire, Montesquieu, and Rousseau.

3 **Summarize** the economic ideas of the physiocrats and Adam Smith.

4 **Describe** how Enlightenment ideas spread and influenced the arts.

5 **Understand** the role of enlightened despots.

Scientific Revolution Leads to the Enlightenment: Text

1. **Determine Central Ideas** Success in science convinced many educated Europeans of the power of human reason. How did an emphasis on human reason lead to developments in other areas of life?

Hobbes and Locke on the Role of Government: Text

2. **Draw Conclusions** Thomas Hobbes argued that people entered into a social contract, an agreement by which they gave up their freedom for an organized society. Give two examples of how we must give up absolute freedom to live in an ordered society.

3. **Draw Conclusions** John Locke proposed that if a government fails in its obligations, the people have the right to overthrow their government. What are some of the obligations you believe a government owes to its people?

The *Philosophes:* Text

4. **Analyze Interactions** Which of the Enlightenment thinkers described in this section had the greatest influence on the actual structure of the U.S. government? What was his contribution?

5. **Explain an Argument** Read the section under the heading "Rousseau Promotes *The Social Contract*." Rousseau argues that the unequal distribution of property was fundamental to corrupting the basic goodness of people in their natural state. Why might people be "corrupted" by an unequal distribution of property?

6. **Draw Inferences** Denis Diderot wanted his 28-volume *Encyclopedia* to change the general way of thinking." What would Diderot think of modern-day versions that solicit user-generated entries, such as Wikipedia? Do such versions undermine or support his original purpose in creating his *Encyclopedia*?

New Economic Ideas: Text

7. **Determine Central Ideas** What are two differences between the physiocrats and the mercantilists?

Spread of Enlightenment Ideas: Text

8. **Identify Key Steps in a Process** List three ways Enlightenment ideas spread during the 1700s.

Interactive Reading Notepad • Lesson 4

Arts and Literature of the Enlightenment: Text

9. **Draw Conclusions** Explain why the *philosophes* criticized rococo art.

10. **Cite Evidence** How did the middle class influence the arts, literature, and music of the period? Support your ideas with examples from the reading.

The Enlightened Despots: Text

11. **Analyze Interactions** The enlightened despots were absolute rulers who used their power to bring about political and social change. Who might object to the political and social change of an enlightened despot?

12. **Draw Inferences** Look back through the reading and find one reform that all three enlightened despots enacted. Why do you believe this reform was a universal theme among these absolute rulers?

Absolutism and Revolution

Lesson 5 The American Revolution

Key Terms

George III
Stamp Act
George Washington
Benjamin Franklin
Thomas Jefferson
popular sovereignty

Yorktown, Virginia
Treaty of Paris
James Madison
federal republic
checks and balances

Academic Vocabulary

assert: to insist on being recognized
monopoly: control of market supply
fundamental: basic; central
supreme: above all others; in highest degree

Lesson Objectives

1 **Describe** how Britain became a global power.

2 **Understand** the events and ideas leading up to the American Revolution, including the impact of the Enlightenment.

3 **Summarize** key events of the American Revolution.

4 **Identify** the political and legal ideas in the Declaration of Independence and the United States Constitution.

Britain Becomes a Global Power: Text

1. **Analyze Interactions** If you were a member of the British Parliament in the 1760s, would you have supported George III's attempt to consolidate power? Explain your answer.

The British Colonies in America: Text

2. **Vocabulary: Determine Meaning** Reread the paragraph that discusses the Navigation Acts. Using the context of the paragraph, what does the term *mercantilist* mean?

Discontent in the Colonies: Text

3. **Determine Central Ideas** Why do you think that the Enlightenment ideals of liberty and equality had such a major influence on the American colonists when they declared themselves independent of Great Britain?

4. **Summarize** What made the Declaration of Independence such a radical document?

5. **Draw Conclusions** If you were a colonial merchant in 1776, would you have supported the Declaration of Independence? Explain why or why not.

The American Revolution: Text

6. **Summarize** In what ways did the French help the Americans against the British?

The United States Constitution: Text

7. **Identify Cause and Effect** How did the ideas of the Enlightenment impact the U.S. Constitution's Bill of Rights?

8. **Summarize** Explain why the U.S. Constitution has been called a "progressive" document.

9. **Determine Meaning** Read the first paragraph of "Symbol of Freedom." What do you think the term *oppressive regimes* means?

Absolutism and Revolution

Lesson 6 The French Revolution Begins

Key Terms

ancien régime	cahier
estate	Tennis Court Oath
bourgeoisie	Bastille
deficit spending	faction
Louis XVI	Marquis de Lafayette
Jacques Necker	Olympe de Gouges
Estates-General	Marie Antoinette

Academic Vocabulary

urban: of, relating to, or characteristic of a city

tithe: one tenth of a person's income paid annually to support a church

feudal: relating to the political and economic system in which a powerful lord granted his vassal a fief or estate to work on in exchange for a pledge of loyalty

proclaimed: announced officially

Lesson Objectives

1 **Describe** the social divisions of France's old order.

2 **Trace** the causes of the French Revolution.

3 **Identify** the reforms enacted by the National Assembly, including the Declaration of the Rights of Man and of the Citizen.

The Old Regime in France: Text

1. **Analyze Interactions** If you were a member of the Third Estate, how would your life be different from the life of a member of the Second Estate? Explain your answer.

2. **Cite Evidence** How did access to government differ among the First, Second, and Third Estates?

3. **Compare and Contrast** Explain the diversity of the Third Estate with regard to income and occupation.

4. **Summarize** What reasons did the Third Estate use to push for social and economic change?

France's Economic Crisis: Text

5. **Identify Cause and Effect** In what way was Louis XVI's attitude toward France's economic conditions a cause of the French Revolution?

6. **Identify Supporting Details** How did the king and First and Second Estates differ over calling the Estates-General?

Louis XVI Calls the Estates-General: Text

7. **Cite Evidence** Louis XVI asked each Estate to draw up a list of grievances. How did the Third Estate use these cahiers for their own benefit?

8. **Draw Inferences** Why do you think the writings of Voltaire, Rousseau, and other *philosophes* influenced the members of the Third Estate more than those of the First and Second Estates?

9. **Identify Cause and Effect** Why was it important for the Third Estate to have the Estates-General meet as a single body?

10. **Summarize** Explain why the Tennis Court Oath was a critical moment on the road to rebellion.

Storming the Bastille: Text

11. **Summarize** Describe the significance of the Bastille and the events of July 14, 1789.

12. **Draw Conclusions** Why do you think that violence, such as the storming of the Bastille, is usually a main component of political revolutions?

Revolts in Paris and the Provinces: Text

13. Summarize What were some of the major events of the "Great Fear"?

The National Assembly: Text

14. Paraphrase When the National Assembly abolished feudalism, the president of the Assembly declared, "We may view this moment as the dawn of a new revolution, when all the burdens weighing on the people were abolished, and France was truly reborn"? What do you think he meant?

15. Draw Conclusions Explain why France's revolutionaries used the motto "Liberty, Fraternity, Equality."

16. Compare and Contrast In what ways did the American Revolution influence the French Revolution?

Reforms of the National Assembly: Text

17. Explain an Argument Why would a member of the bourgeoisie distrust the clergy?

18. Draw Inferences What changes did the Constitution of 1791 bring to the French government? Which of these changes reflected the goals of the Enlightenment?

Absolutism and Revolution

Lesson 7 A Radical Phase

Key Terms

émigré	Reign of Terror
sans-culottes	guillotine
Jacobin	Napoleon Bonaparte
suffrage	nationalism
Maximilien Robespierre	Marseilles

Academic Vocabulary

radical: extreme; departure from the usual or traditional

moderate: person in politics who is not excessive or unreasonable

dictatorial: imposing will on others

suppress: to prevent something from happening

Lesson Objectives

1 **Explain** why the French Revolution entered a more radical phase.

2 **Understand** how radicals abolished the French monarchy.

3 **Analyze** the causes and course of the Reign of Terror.

4 **Describe** France under the Directory.

5 **Identify** how the French Revolution changed life in France.

Radicals Gain Strength: Text

1. Analyze Interactions If you were a European monarch during the French Revolution, why would you fear the "French plague"?

2. Identify Supporting Details What did the Declaration of Pilnitz do?

3. Compare and Contrast Why did the political philosophy of the Jacobins throw the Revolution into another phase?

The Monarchy Is Abolished: Text

4. Paraphrase Explain the meaning of the excerpt below from a statement given by King Louis XVI prior to his execution: "Frenchmen, I die innocent. I pardon the authors of my death. I pray God that the blood about to be spilt will never fall upon the head of France."

The Reign of Terror: Text

5. Draw Inferences What was the result of Robespierre's desire to achieve a "republic of virtue"?

6. **Paraphrase** Explain in your own words what Robespierre meant when he said: "The first maxim of our politics ought to be to lead the people by means of reason and the enemies of the people by terror . . . If the basis of popular government in time of peace is virtue, the basis of popular government in time of revolution is both virtue and terror."

Reaction and the Directory: Text

7. **Determine Central Ideas** What was the main impact of the Constitution of 1795?

The Revolution Transforms France: Text

8. **Summarize** In what ways did the French Revolution change France?

9. **Draw Inferences** Explain why, during the Revolution, the French wore practical clothes as opposed to the elaborate fashions they once wore in pre-revolutionary times.

10. **Compare and Contrast** In what ways was the American Revolution similar to the French Revolution? In what ways were the revolutions different?

11. **Compare and Contrast** How did America and France react differently to the role of religion in the state?

Absolutism and Revolution

Lesson 8 The Age of Napoleon

Key Terms

plebiscite   guerrilla warfare

Napoleonic Code   abdicate

Napoleonic Wars   Congress of Vienna

annex   legitimacy

Continental System   Concert of Europe

Academic Vocabulary

anticipate: to foresee or expect

coronation: a ceremony in which a member of a royal family becomes king or queen

despotism: the use of power in a cruel and unreasonable way

Lesson Objectives

1 **Describe** how Napoleon Bonaparte rose to power.

2 **Explain** the impact of Napoleon and the Napoleonic Wars.

3 **Identify** the reasons for Napoleon's fall from power.

4 **Understand** how the Congress of Vienna tried to restore order to Europe.

Copyright © Pearson Education, Inc., or its affiliates. All Rights Reserved.

Napoleon on the Rise: Text

1. **Draw Conclusions** Napoleon once said: "Since one must take sides, one might as well choose the side that is victorious, the side which devastates, loots, and burns. Considering the alternative, it is better to eat than be eaten." What does this quote indicate about Napoleon's political ambitions and values?

2. **Cite Evidence** What made young Napoleon a popular figure in France?

3. **Identify Cause and Effect** How did Napoleon build his image as a military leader in France?

Napoleon Reforms France: Text

4. **Identify Cause and Effect** Name at least three reforms Napoleon brought to France.

5. **Draw Conclusions** Why would most people welcome Napoleon's decision to open up government jobs based on talent?

6. **Compare and Contrast** What did the Napoleonic Code have in common with the principles of the Enlightenment? How did Napoleon's rule violate Enlightenment principles?

The Napoleonic Wars: Text

7. **Draw Inferences** What does this quote indicate about Napoleon's reputation as a military genius? "I grew up on the field of battle, and a man such as I am cares little for the life of a million men."

8. **Draw Conclusions** In the section titled, "Redrawing the Map of Europe," what does the text mean when it uses the term "forceful diplomacy"?

9. **Summarize** The Continental System did not work. Why?

Challenges to the French Empire: Text

10. **Summarize** At first some Europeans welcomed Napoleon in their countries. Why did they eventually turn against him?

Napoleon Falls from Power: Text

11. **Analyze Interactions** If you were a citizen of France in 1814, would you have welcomed Napoleon back from his exile? Explain your answer.

The Congress of Vienna: Text

12. **Analyze Interactions** What were the major outcomes of the Congress of Vienna?

The Industrial Revolution

Lesson 1 The Industrial Revolution Begins

Key Terms

Industrial Revolution	entrepreneur
anesthetic	putting-out system
enclosure	Eli Whitney
James Watt	turnpike
smelt	Liverpool
capital	Manchester
enterprise	

Academic Vocabulary

Illuminate: to light up; to give light to

Dominate: to rule or control by power or influence

Lesson Objectives

1 **Describe** how changes in agriculture helped spark the Industrial Revolution.

2 **Analyze** why the Industrial Revolution began in Britain.

3 **Explain** the role of steam technology and textile manufacturing in the Industrial Revolution.

4 **Describe** how the factory system and transportation revolution advanced industry.

5 **Trace** how the Industrial Revolution spread.

New Ways of Working Change Life: Text

1. **Compare and Contrast** As you read, fill out a diagram like the one below. In the diagram, identify characteristics of how people lived before and after the Industrial Revolution.

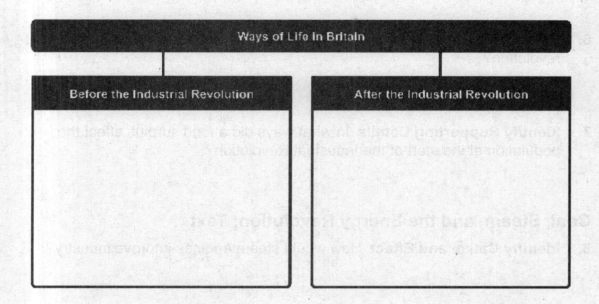

Ways of Life In Britain

| Before the Industrial Revolution | After the Industrial Revolution |

2. **Analyze Interactions** How did the Scientific Revolution of the seventeenth century lead to the Industrial Revolution?

3. **Draw Conclusions** During the 1750s, before the Industrial Revolution, why did most people see little of the world?

4. **Vocabulary: Determine Meaning** Reread the text under "A Rural Way of Life," and notice the adjective *rural*. What does *rural* mean? Provide an antonym for the word *rural* along with three examples of a "rural way of life" before the Industrial Revolution.

Interactive Reading Notepad • Lesson 1

A New Agricultural Revolution: Text

5. **Evaluate Explanations** Reread the first paragraph to answer the following. What was the first agricultural revolution? Why were the changes that took place in agriculture in the 1700s considered a "second" agricultural revolution?

6. **Summarize** Why did the population of villages shrink during the agricultural revolution?

7. **Identify Supporting Details** In what ways did a food surplus affect the population at the start of the Industrial Revolution?

Coal, Steam, and the Energy Revolution: Text

8. **Identify Cause and Effect** How would steam engines improve industry?

9. **Draw Inferences** Why was coal a vital power source? What effect might it have on employment?

Why Did the Industrial Revolution Start in Britain?: Text

10. **Draw Conclusions** How did Britain's overseas empire contribute to its role in starting the Industrial Revolution?

11. **Identify Cause and Effect** What role did wealthy investors play in promoting the Industrial Revolution?

12. **Summarize** Explain how the four factors of production are each needed in order to produce goods.

Textile Industry Initiates Industrialization: Text

13. Analyze Sequence Why did the flying shuttle require the invention of the spinning jenny?

14. Draw Inferences How did Eli Whitney help the economy of the American South?

15. Draw Conclusions What was the relationship between the invention of the water frame and the location of the earliest sheds used for manufacturing? Why were early steam-powered factories built in locations that were different from those of the earliest sheds?

A Revolution in Transportation: Text

16. Analyze Sequence Review the text. Then describe the sequence of improvements in transportation, and explain how each improvement contributed to the Industrial Revolution.

17. Analyze Interactions Explain how iron production and railroading are interrelated.

Industrialization Spreads: Text

18. Identify Supporting Details How did Britain try to maintain its lead as the first to industrialize?

19. Draw Inferences After the new inventions of the textile industry reached the United States, what advantages did the United States have over Britain?

The Industrial Revolution

Lesson 2 Social Impact of Industrialism

Key Terms

urbanization

tenement

labor union

standard of living

social mobility

free market

Thomas Malthus

Jeremy Bentham

utilitarianism

socialism

means of production

Robert Owen

Karl Marx

communism

proletariat

social democracy

Academic Vocabulary

contaminated: unclean and impure; polluted

formulated: devised or developed, as in a theory or plan

stressed: emphasized

Lesson Objectives

1 **Outline** the growth of industrial cities and the emergence of new social classes.

2 **Describe** the working conditions in factories and mines.

3 **Analyze** the benefits and challenges of industrialism.

4 **Describe** ideas Adam Smith and other thinkers regarding free enterprise.

5 **Identify** the origins and characteristics of socialism and communism.

Industry Causes Urban Growth: Text

1. **Draw Conclusions** What local characteristics were most likely to make towns and villages grow in population during the Industrial Revolution?

2. **Summarize** Describe the city of Manchester after industrialization.

The Rise of New Social Classes: Text

3. **Vocabulary: Determine Meaning** Reread the text under "The Lives of the New Middle Class." What is meant by the phrase *rags to riches*?

4. **Compare and Contrast** What was life like for the middle class compared to the working class?

5. **Vocabulary: Use Context Clues** Today, the term *Luddite* refers to people who are against using the latest technology. Why is this a historically appropriate term?

6. **Draw Inferences** Why was John Wesley's message attractive to working class people?

Harsh Conditions in Factories and Mines: Text

7. **Identify Supporting Details** Why did factory owners seek out women to employ?

8. **Draw Inferences** In what ways was mining dangerous? Why did people continue to work in mines despite the dangers?

9. **Explain an Argument** Why do you think child labor was considered acceptable during the Industrial Revolution?

Benefits of the Industrial Revolution: Text

10. **Analyze Interactions** Reread the text under the heading "Better Standards of Living." Explain the relationship between price and supply, and how this affected people's standard of living during the Industrial Revolution.

11. **Cite Evidence** In what way is the story of Josiah Wedgwood an example of the success of free market enterprise?

Laissez-Faire Economics: Text

12. **Vocabulary: Use Context Clues** Why does "laissez-faire" describe free-enterprise capitalism?

13. **Analyze Interactions** In what way did Malthus believe poverty and population were connected?

14. **Cite Evidence** In what way was Malthus proved wrong?

Utilitarians Support Limited Government: Text

15. **Vocabulary: Determine Meaning** Identify words that have a root word similar to that of *utilitarianism*. How are the definitions of these words related?

16. **Determine Author's Point of View** What did John Stuart Mill mean by saying, "The only purpose for which power can be rightfully exercised over any member of a civilized community, against his will, is to prevent harm to others"?

Socialist Thought Emerges: Text

17. **Identify Supporting Details** Reread the first paragraph of the section "The Socialist Point of View." What are the characteristics of socialism that could make it "a radical solution"?

18. **Determine Central Ideas** What was Robert Owen's main goal in setting up a Utopian community at New Lanark?

Marx and the Origins of Communism: Text

19. **Summarize** Marx predicted the proletariat would rise up and overthrow the bourgeoisie. What system did he think would replace the current economic system, and what were its characteristics? Support your answer with details from the text.

20. **Draw Inferences** Why did workers fail to unite and form successful communist societies?

Interactive Reading Notepad • Lesson 2

The Industrial Revolution

Lesson 3 The Second Industrial Revolution

Key Terms

Henry Bessemer	corporation
Alfred Nobel	cartel
Michael Faraday	germ theory
dynamo	Louis Pasteur
Thomas Edison	Robert Koch
interchangeable parts	Florence Nightingale
assembly line	Joseph Lister
Orville and Wilbur Wright	urban renewal
Guglielmo Marconi	mutual-aid society
stock	

Academic Vocabulary

illuminate: to rule or control by power or influence

Lesson Objectives

1 **Describe** the impact of new technology on industry, transportation, and communication.

2 **Understand** how big business emerged.

3 **Summarize** the impact of medical advances in the later 1800s.

4 **Describe** how cities changed and grew.

5 **Explain** how conditions for workers gradually improved.

Science and Technology Change Industry: Text

1. **Identify Cause and Effect** As you read "Science and Technology Change Industry," use this graphic organizer to list the inventions and new methods under causes, and then record the effects of each one.

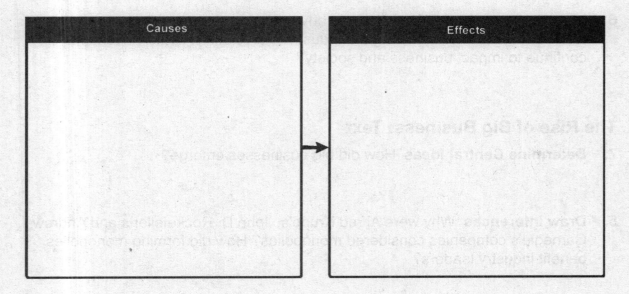

Causes	Effects

2. **Integrate Information From Diverse Sources** Reread "The Bessemer Process Transforms Steel." How did steel production change between 1880 and 1910? Why do you think industrialized countries begin to measure their success by their steel output?

3. **Draw Conclusions** Why was Michael Faraday's dynamo essential to later inventions, such as the light bulb, and new industrial processes? Cite evidence from the text to support your answer.

Advances in Transportation and Communication: Text

4. **Draw Inferences** Why did industrialized nations build transcontinental railroads? How did expanding railroads affect the economy and people's way of life?

Interactive Reading Notepad • Lesson 3

5. **Draw Conclusions** Explain the evolution of the automobile. Why did Henry Ford become the leader in the automobile industry? Cite textual evidence to support your response.

6. **Identify Cause and Effect** How did advances in communication impact the world and the economy during the Industrial Revolution? Which inventions continue to impact business and society?

The Rise of Big Business: Text

7. **Determine Central Ideas** How did big businesses emerge?

8. **Draw Inferences** Why were Alfred Krupp's, John D. Rockefeller's and Andrew Carnegie's companies considered monopolies? How did forming monopolies benefit industry leaders?

9. **Explain an Argument** Why was there a debate over the growth of big business? Explain both sides of the argument. Cite textual evidence to support your response.

10. **Cite Evidence** Why was it difficult to regulate large corporations and monopolies? Cite textual evidence to support your response.

Better Medicine, Nutrition, and Health: Text

11. **Identify Cause and Effect** Why did the population in Europe more than double during the 19th century? How was this rapid growth in population different from previous population explosions? Cite evidence from the text to support your response.

12. **Identify Supporting Details** What was the germ theory? How did Louis Pasteur's work help prove the theory and impact later advances in medicine?

13. **Identify Cause and Effect** Identify some of the medical advances during the late 1800s. What impact did these medical advances have on human life?

City Life Changes: Text

14. **Compare and Contrast** How did Paris look before George Haussmann redesigned it? What was the effect of the new design?

15. **Draw Conclusions** Why was the spread of disease a problem in industrial cities in the mid-1800s? What changes did people make to try to stop epidemics?

16. **Compare and Contrast** Why did the poor live closer to city centers than the middle class did? How might the middle and upper classes have experienced city life differently than the working class did?

The Working Class Wins New Rights: Text

17. **Draw Conclusions** Why was it important that workers won the right to organize unions? How did this right affect working conditions?

18. **Determine Central Ideas** What reform had the British coal miners won by 1909 in Britain? What reforms did Germany and other Western governments pass in the early 1900s? How did these changes affect workers? Cite textual evidence to support your response.

The Industrial Revolution

Lesson 4 Changing Ways of Life and Thought

Key Terms

cult of domesticity	Lord Byron
temperance movement	Victor Hugo
Elizabeth Cady Stanton	Ludwig van Beethoven
women's suffrage	realism
Sojourner Truth	Charles Dickens
John Dalton	Gustave Courbet
Charles Darwin	Louis Daguerre
racism	impressionism
social gospel	Claude Monet
romanticism	Vincent van Gogh
William Wordsworth	

Academic Vocabulary

speculate: to think about

controversial: that is or can be argued about or debated

emphasis: special attention given to something to make it stand out

intense: very strong or deep

Lesson Objectives

1 **Identify** what values shaped the new social order.

2 **Describe** how the role of women changed in the Industrial Revolution.

3 **Explain** the impact of education, new scientific ideas, and religion.

4 **Analyze** how romanticism, realism, and impressionism reflected the culture of the Industrial Age.

The New Social Order: Text

1. **Determine Central Ideas** How did the Industrial Revolution change the social order in the Western world?

2. **Summarize** Describe the changing roles of people in middle-class families during the Industrial Revolution.

The Struggle for Women's Rights: Text

3. **Summarize** What was the temperance movement? Summarize why women's groups supported the temperance movement. Use evidence from the text to support your answer.

4. **Identify Cause and Effect** How did women's involvement in the abolition movement lead to some women campaigning for voting rights?

The Rise of Public Education: Text

5. **Draw Inferences** What skills did schools begin to teach beyond academics? Why did they begin teaching these skills?

6. **Compare and Contrast** How did the education of girls compare with the education of boys? Why did girls and boys receive different educations?

New Directions in Science: Text

7. **Identify Cause and Effect** How did the work of John Dalton influence Dmitri Mendeleyev? Why was their work so important?

Interactive Reading Notepad • Lesson 4

8. **Determine Central Ideas** What new sciences and discoveries challenged long-held beliefs about the age of the Earth? Why were these ideas controversial?

9. **Draw Conclusions** Why were Charles Darwin's ideas controversial?

The Role of Religion: Text

10. **Draw Inferences** Why did living conditions in industrialized nations encourage compassionate and charitable feelings among some people?

The Romantics Turn from Reason: Text

11. **Determine Central Ideas** Reread the lines from William Wordsworth's poem:

> It is a beauteous evening, calm and free,
> The holy time is quiet as a Nun
> Breathless with adoration; the broad sun
> Is sinking down in its tranquility
> —William Wordsworth, *Complete Poetical Works*

What values does this poem reflect? How did these values contrast with the values of the Enlightenment and the Industrial Age?

12. **Analyze Interactions** How did Beethoven's music reflect romanticism? Cite examples from the text to support your response.

13. **Make Inferences** What themes inspired many romantic writers and architects? Why might they have found these ideas inspirational?

Artists Represent Real Life: Text

14. Draw Conclusions What subjects did realist writers typically focus on in their novels? Why did they focus on these people and things?

15. Identify Cause and Effect How did members of the middle class respond to the realist movement? Why did they respond this way?

16. Draw Conclusions Painter Gustave Courbet once said, "I cannot paint an angel because I have never seen one." What did he mean by this? How does this statement express the ideas of the realist movement?

New Directions in the Visual Arts: Text

17. Draw Conclusions How was photography used to support reform efforts? Why do you think it was an effective tool?

18. Compare and Contrast How does impressionist painting differ from realist painting?

Nationalism and the Spread of Democracy

Lesson 1 Revolutions Sweep Europe

Key Terms

ideology	Louis Philippe
universal manhood suffrage	recession
autonomy	Napoleon III
radical	Louis Kossuth
absolutism	

Academic Vocabulary

agitator: someone who attempts to arouse feeling for or against something

denounce: to express harsh criticism of something or somebody

emerge: to arise, appear, or come out of

Lesson Objectives

1 **Compare** the goals of conservatives and liberals in 19th century Europe.

2 **Identify** the influence of liberty, equality, and nationalism on political revolutions.

3 **Describe** the causes and results of the revolutions of 1830 and 1848.

A Clash of Ideologies: Text

1. **Determine Central Ideas** Explain what Prince Metternich meant by the seed of revolution. Cite evidence from the text to support your answer.

2. **Cite Evidence** List three reasons why Conservatives preferred the old order. Cite evidence from the text to support your answer.

Liberalism and Nationalism Spur Revolts: Text

3. **Determine Central Ideas** As you read "A Clash of Ideologies" and "Liberals and Nationalists Spur Revolt," use this graphic organizer to list the characteristics of conservatism, liberalism, and nationalism.

Liberalism	Nationalism	Conservatism
• •	• •	• •

4. **Summarize** Explain why Liberals supported laissez-faire economics.

Rebellions Erupt in Eastern Europe: Text

5. **Compare** How were the revolts in Serbia, Greece, Spain, Portugal, and the Italian states similar? What ideals did the revolutionaries have in common?

6. **Identify Main Ideas** Reread the quote from Prince Metternich. What events proved that Metternich was correct in his fears?

Revolutions of 1830 and 1848: Text

7. **Identify Cause and Effect** Explain the causes that led to the French Revolution of 1830.

8. **Draw Inferences** After Charles X fled to England, radicals and liberals had different ideas about how to establish the new French government. Explain their differences and how these differences impacted the Revolution of 1848.

Demands for Reform Spread: Text

9. **Compare and Contrast** Fill in the Venn diagram below with information about the Belgian and Polish uprisings. What factor most affected the outcome of the two revolutions?

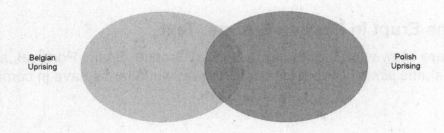

Belgian Uprising   Polish Uprising

10. **Cite Evidence** from this text that supports Metternich's saying, "When France sneezes, Europe catches a cold."

The Revolution of 1848 in France: Text

11. **Compare and Contrast** How were the "February Days" and the "June Days" similar and different?

12. **Draw Inferences** The revolutions of 1830 and 1848 were the result of new ways of thinking and hard times for workers. Could one of these factors by itself have caused such widespread rebellion? Why or why not?

Revolution Spreads Across Europe: Text

13. **Identify Cause and Effect** List two causes and two effects of the 1848 revolutions in Europe. Use evidence from the text to support your answer.

14. **Draw Conclusions** Why were most of the rebellions in 1848 unsuccessful?

Nationalism and the Spread of Democracy

Lesson 2 Latin American Nations Win Independence

Key Terms

peninsular
creole
mestizo
mulatto
Simón Bolívar

Toussaint L'Ouverture
Father Miguel Hidalgo
Father José Morelos
José de San Martín
Dom Pedro

Academic Vocabulary

cement: to secure or form a strong bond

proclaim: to announce publically or formally

Lesson Objectives

1 **List** the causes of growing discontent in Latin America, including the influence of the Enlightenment.

2 **Trace** the influence of the American and French revolutions on Latin America.

3 **Describe** the revolutions in Haiti, Mexico, and Central America.

4 **Explain** how South American nations won independence, including the role of Simón Bolívar.

Latin America Ripe for Revolution: Text

1. **Determine Central Ideas** As you read "Latin America Ripe for Revolution" fill in the pyramid below. Describe the members of each social class and the powers they had. Then describe how this social structure caused problems in Latin America.

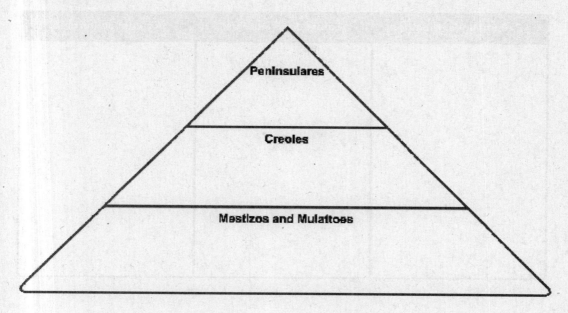

Peninsulares

Creoles

Mestizos and Mulattoes

2. **Draw Conclusions** How did the American Revolution impact the revolutions in Latin America?

Haiti's Fight for Freedom: Text

3. **Identify Supporting Details** What led enslaved Haitians to revolt and fight with Toussaint L'Ouverture for independence?

4. **Draw Conclusions** How might the Haitian Revolution have ended if French soldiers did not have to battle yellow fever?

Revolts in Mexico and Central America: Text

5. **Identify Supporting Details** Fill in the chart below with details about how these revolutionary leaders helped to free Mexico and Central America.

Father Miguel Hidalgo	Father José Morelos	Agustin de Iturbide

6. **Compare** How did Iturbide's motive for rebellion differ from the motives of Father Hidalgo and Father Morelos?

7. **Cause and Effect** How did events in Spain affect the fight for Mexican independence?

Discontent Sparks Revolts in South America: Text

8. **Draw Conclusions** Why was Bolívar's plan to march his army across the Andes considered daring?

9. **Evaluate Explanations** What did Bolívar mean when he wrote, "We achieved our independence at the expense of everything else"?

Nationalism and the Spread of Democracy

Lesson 3 The Unification of Germany

Key Terms

Otto von Bismarck

chancellor

Realpolitik

annex

kaiser

Reich

Kulturkampf

William II

social welfare

Academic Vocabulary

edit: to make additions, deletions, or other changes to a piece of writing

synthetic: prepared or made artificially

coordinate: to design or adjust to create harmonious action

Lesson Objectives

1 **Identify** the factors that promoted German nationalism.

2 **Analyze** how Bismarck achieved German unification.

3 **Describe** the German empire under Bismarck.

4 **Explain** the policies of Kaiser William II.

Moving Toward a Unified Germany: Text

1. **Draw Conclusions** How did Napoleon's invasions affect Germany?

2. **Identify Cause and Effect** What economic changes in the 1830s promoted German unity?

Bismarck Becomes the Architect of German Unity: Text

3. **Identify Supporting Details** Explain how Bismarck's persistence in strengthening the Prussian army helped to unify Germany.

4. **Draw Conclusions** How did the emperor and his chancellor retain power in the new German government?

Germany Becomes an Industrial Giant: Text

5. **Identify Supporting Details** What factors allowed Germany to grow into an industrial giant?

6. **Identify Cause and Effect** How did the German government support economic development?

The Iron Chancellor: Text

7. **Determine Central Ideas** Identify the origins of socialism in Germany.

8. **Analyze Word Choices** Why was Bismarck known as the "Iron Chancellor"?

Kaiser William II: Text

9. **Compare and Contrast** List two ways that Bismarck and Kaiser William II were similar and one way they were different.

10. **Draw Conclusions** How do you think Bismarck may have felt about being asked to resign?

Nationalism and the Spread of Democracy

Lesson 4 The Unification of Italy

Key Terms
Camillo Cavour   anarchist

Giuseppe Garibaldi   emigration

Academic Vocabulary

constitute: to set up; establish

agitation: the attempt to arouse public feeling about an issue

successor: a person who succeeds another to an office or rank

---

Lesson Objectives

1 **List** the key obstacles to Italian unity.

2 **Evaluate** the roles played by Cavour and Garibaldi in Italian unification.

3 **Describe** the challenges that faced the new nation of Italy.

First Steps to Italian Unity: Text

1. **Determine Author's Point of View** What did Mazzini mean by this quote: "Ideas grow quickly when watered by the blood of martyrs"?

2. **Categorize** List the geographic, cultural, and economic reasons for Italian unification.

The Struggle for Italy: Text

3. **Compare and Contrast** How were the views of Cavour, Mazzini, and Garibaldi alike? How were they different?

4. **Analyze Interactions** Why did Sardinia ally itself first with France and then, later, with Prussia against France?

5. **Draw Inferences** Why did Garibaldi give Naples and Sicily to Victor Emmanuel?

Italy Faces New Challenges: Text

6. **Compare and Contrast** Use this graphic organizer to compare and contrast the regional differences of northern and southern Italy.

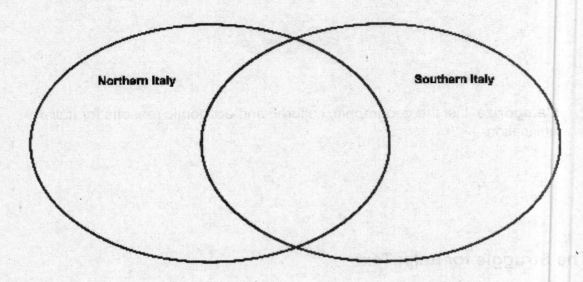

Northern Italy   Southern Italy

7. **Cite Evidence** How did the Italian government try to contain political unrest in the late 1800s?

Interactive Reading Notepad • Lesson 4

Nationalism and the Spread of Democracy

Lesson 5 Democratic Reforms in Britain

Key Terms

rotten borough	free trade
electorate	repeal
secret ballot	abolition movement
Queen Victoria	capital offense
Benjamin Disraeli	penal colony
William Gladstone	absentee landlord
parliamentary democracy	home rule

Academic Vocabulary

allocate: to distribute according to a plan

drastic: severe, harsh, extreme

Lesson Objectives

1 **Understand** how political reforms in Britain affected suffrage and the nature of Parliament.

2 **Identify** the influence of Queen Victoria and the values she represented.

3 **Describe** social and economic reforms enacted by Parliament in the 1800s.

4 **Describe** the efforts by British women to win the vote.

5 **Explain** the struggle for Irish home rule and the impact of famine on Ireland.

"Two Nations": The Rich and the Poor: Text

1. **Draw Conclusions** Why would expanding democratic rights help to bridge Britain's "two nations"?

2. **Support Ideas with Evidence** Explain why Britain was far from democratic during the early 1800s. Use evidence from the Text to support your answer.

3. **Summarize** How did the Great Reform Act of 1832 change Parliament?

4. **Explain an Argument** Why were the Chartists not satisfied with the democratic reforms of the Great Reform Act of 1832? What did they propose instead?

The Victorian Age: Text

5. **Categorize** What values did Queen Victoria represent, and how did these values relate to economic reform?

Reforms Increase Parliamentary Democracy: Text

6. **Paraphrase** How did the Reform Bill of 1867 affect politics and government?

7. **Summarize** Why did the House of Lords eventually become a largely ceremonial body with little power?

8. **Analyze Interactions** Which group in the early 1800s do you think most feared the "democratization" of Britain? Why?

Economic and Social Reforms: Text

9. **Draw Conclusions** Which British social classes would most benefit from the elimination of tariffs? Why?

10. **Determine Central Issues** How did abolition and criminal justice reform reflect Victorian values?

Victories for the Working Class: Text

11. **Draw Conclusions** Why would the British government make trade unions legal but not allow strikes?

12. **Explain an Argument** Re-read the text under "The Labour Party Emerges." Why do you think the middle class hailed reforms "as proof that democracy was working"?

13. **Cite Evidence** Look through the Text to find examples of three reforms that helped the British working class. Use details to describe each one and the groups affected.

Women Struggle for the Vote: Text

14. **Identify Key Steps in a Process** What tactics did suffragists first try to win the vote?

15. **Analyze Interactions** Why do you think women disagreed about how best to gain suffrage?

16. **Evaluate an Argument** Why do you think the British government force-fed suffragists who went on hunger strikes?

The Irish Question: Text

17. **Identify Cause and Effect** Do you think the Irish famine was a natural disaster or a human-made disaster? Why?

18. **Determine Central Ideas** How did British policies toward Ireland affect the cause of Irish nationalism?

Interactive Reading Notepad

Nationalism and the Spread of Democracy

Lesson 6 Divisions and Democracy in France

Key Terms

Napoleon III

Suez Canal

provisional

premier

coalition

Dreyfus affair

libel

Zionism

Academic Vocabulary

repress: to put down, subdue

Bourgeoisie: middle class

satellite: a country that is controlled by another country

fervor: extreme feeling or emotion

Lesson Objectives

1 **List** the domestic and foreign policies of Napoleon III.

2 **Describe** the challenges and political reforms of the Third Republic.

3 **Explain** how the Dreyfus Affair divided France and contributed to the growth of the Zionist movement.

Napoleon III and the Second Empire: Text

1. **Identify Supporting Details** For what reasons did a wide variety of French people support Napoleon III?

2. **Summarize** What were some of Napoleon III's political reforms?

3. **Cite Evidence** What actions did Mexican patriots take during Napoleon III's rule?

The Third Republic Faces New Struggles: Text

4. **Cite Evidence** In what ways did the Communards hope to change their government?

5. **Synthesize** Why were there 50 different governments in the first 10 years of the Third Republic?

6. **Use Visual Information** Look at the political cartoon about Boulanger. Why did the cartoonist portray Boulanger at the head of a parade?

The Dreyfus Affair: Text

7. **Draw Inferences** What did the Dreyfus Affair reveal about French society?

Reforms in France: Text

8. **Identify Supporting Details** What was the relationship between the Bloc Républicain and the church, and why?

9. **Cite Evidence** What is one possible reason that French women did not get the vote until after World War II? Use information from the text to support your answer.

Nationalism and the Spread of Democracy

Lesson 7 Growth of the United States

Key Terms

expansionism

Louisiana Purchase

Manifest Destiny

secede

segregation

Academic Vocabulary

annex: to add a country or other territory into an existing country or state

resolution: a formal showing of an intent voted by an official group

monopoly: sole ownership or control over a commodity, product, or service

dominate: to rule or control by superior power or influence

Lesson Objectives

1 **Describe** the territorial expansion of the United States.

2 **Summarize** the causes and effects of the Civil War.

3 **Explain** how American democracy grew in the 1800s.

4 **Analyze** the impact of economic growth and social reform on the United States.

The United States Expands: Text

1. **Identify Cause and Effect** What is expansionism, and how did a policy of expansionism affect the United States?

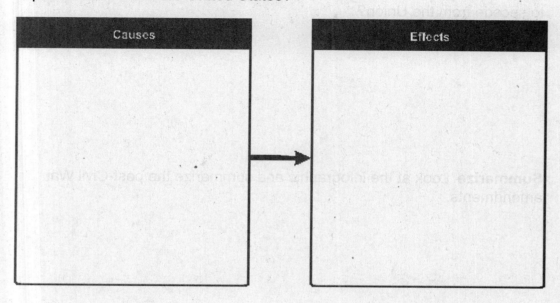

| Causes | Effects |

Expanding Democracy: Text

2. **Cite Evidence** Describe how the electorate changed during the 1800s. Be sure to cite dates from the text.

3. **Determine Central Ideas** How did the expansion of the United States affect the issue of slavery?

4. **Analyze Interactions** How did involvement in the abolition movement help launch the fight for women's rights?

The Civil War: Text

5. Identify Cause and Effect What were the main differences between the Northern and Southern states, and what ultimately caused the Southern states to secede from the Union?

6. Summarize Look at the infographic and summarize the post-Civil War amendments.

Economic Growth and Reform: Text

7. Explain What factors helped the United States become an agricultural and industrial leader? Choose one factor and explain its influence.

8. Identify Supporting Details How did the Populist Party influence reform in the United States?

Nationalism and the Spread of Democracy

Lesson 8 Nationalism in Eastern Europe and Russia

Key Terms

Francis Joseph

Ferenc Deák

Dual Monarchy

colossus

Alexander II

Crimean War

emancipation

zemstvo

pogrom

refugees

Duma

Peter Stolypin

Academic Vocabulary

fraternal: brotherly

radical: a person who favors great changes or reforms

persecution: harassment or hostile treatment of a group or person because of belief

---

Lesson Objectives

1 Explain how nationalism challenged Austria and the Ottoman Empire.

2 Summarize major obstacles to progress in Russia.

3 Describe the cycle of absolutism, reform, and reaction followed by the tsars.

4 Explain how industrialization contributed to the outbreak of revolution in 1905.

Nationalism Endangers Old Empires: Text

1. **Identify Cause and Effect** Why did industrialization challenge the rule of the Hapsburgs, and what was the result?

2. **Determine Central Ideas** What reforms did Francis Joseph institute after the empire's defeat by France and Sardinia? Why did these reforms not ease tensions?

The Dual Monarchy: Text

3. **Draw Inferences** Why was the Dual Monarchy an insufficient compromise?

The Ottoman Empire Declines: Text

4. **Draw Inferences** Why was the Ottoman Empire called the "sick man of Europe"?

Russia Tries Reform: Text

5. **Cite Evidence** Citing evidence from the text, describe the extent of the Russian empire in the 1800s.

6. **Analyze Interactions** Describe the different levels in Russian society and their interactions with one another.

Emancipation and Stirrings of Revolution: Text

7. **Draw Conclusions** The text states that Alexander II's reign "represents the pattern of reform and repression used by his father and grandfather, Alexander I and Nicholas I." How is this true? Use the text to cite specific examples.

8. **Determine Central Ideas** What event was the catalyst for reform during Alexander II's reign, and what did it show?

9. **Summarize** What was "Russification," and why did it increase nationalism?

The Beginnings of Industrialization: Text

10. **Draw Conclusions** Why did railroads help countries such as Russia industrialize and grow economically?

11. **Draw Inferences** Why did radicals find "fertile ground" in Russia in the late nineteenth and early twentieth centuries?

The Road to Revolution: Text

12. **Determine Central Ideas** Why did Stolypin's reforms fail to ease the tension in Russia?

The Age of Imperialism

Lesson 1 The New Imperialism

Key Terms
imperialism

sphere of influence

protectorate

Academic Vocabulary

prestige: the power to impress or influence because of success or wealth

Lesson Objectives

1 **Explain** the political, economic, and social causes of European imperialism.

2 **Understand** how technology and other factors contributed to the spread of imperialism.

3 **Describe** the characteristics of imperial rule.

4 **Summarize** the cultural, political, and economic effects of imperialism.

Motivations for the New Imperialism: Text

Identify Cause and Effect As you read "Motivations for the New Imperialism," use this graphic organizer to record multiple causes of the New Imperialism.

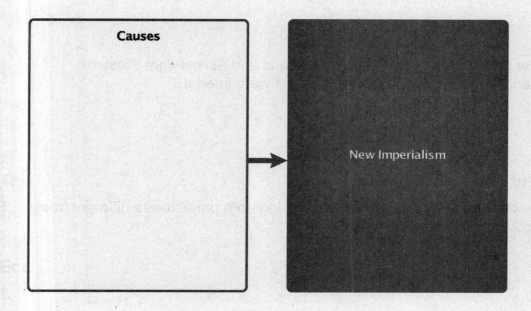

1. **Compare and Contrast** Read the first three paragraphs of the text. How was Western imperialism in the 1800s similar to European imperialism in the three previous centuries? How was it different?

2. **Vocabulary: Use Context Clues** Read the paragraph under the heading "Need for Resources Drives Further Expansion." Based on its context, what do you think the word *ventures* means? How did Western bankers seeking *ventures* for profit have an effect on imperialism?

Western Imperialism Spreads Rapidly: Text

3. **Identify Supporting Details** What details under "Western Advantages" support the idea that superior weaponry helped Western imperialism spread?

4. **Draw Inferences** Why did some Africans and Asians fight Western imperialism, even though their weapons were inferior?

Types of Imperial Rule: Text

5. **Compare and Contrast** How was setting up a protectorate different from practicing direct rule?

6. **Draw Conclusions** Why did European countries sometimes choose to maintain spheres of influence instead of creating colonies?

The Effects of Imperialism: Text

7. **Identify Cause and Effect** As European power spread, so did European ideas. Reread the paragraph under "Political Changes." What European idea led to colonial resistance?

8. **Draw Inferences** What problems might an outside country create if it draws borders without understanding local political or ethnic situations?

The Age of Imperialism

Lesson 2 European Colonies in Africa

Key Terms

Usman dan Fodio

Shaka

paternalistic

David Livingstone

Henry Stanley

King Leopold II

Boer War

Samori Touré

Yaa Asantewaa

Nehanda

Menelik II

elite

Academic Vocabulary

domain: territory over which rule or control is exercised

exploited: taken advantage of

Lesson Objectives

1 **Describe** the forces that shaped Africa in the early 1800s.

2 **Explain** why European contact with Africa increased.

3 **Analyze** how European nations carved up Africa.

4 **Describe** African resistance to imperialism.

Africa Before Imperialism: Text

1. **Predict Consequences** What was the state of the Ottoman empire in the early 1800s? How might that influence events in North Africa?

2. **Compare and Contrast** conditions in West Africa to those in East Africa in the early 1800s.

3. **Analyze Interactions** How did the fact that the British took control of Cape Colony in Southern Africa affect developments in the region?

European Contact Increases: Text

4. **Cite Evidence** Why did the first Europeans to travel into the interior of Africa make the journey?

5. **Hypothesize** According to the text, missionaries wanted to help Africans while they tried to convert them to Christianity. Why might they have believed that opening Africa to Western ways would improve life for Africans?

European Nations Scramble for Colonies: Text

Identify Cause and Effect As you read "European Nations Scramble for Colonies," examine the text for major events and their causes and effects. Then use a chart like this one to record major events, as well as their causes and effects.

Event	Cause	Effect
France conquers Tunisia and takes colonies in West and Central Africa.		
British industrialist Cecil Rhodes helps Britain extend its empire by 1,000,000 miles.		
British form Union of South Africa from Cape Colony and former Boer republics.		
Portuguese gain colonies in Angola and Mozambique.		
Italy occupies Libya and seeks to rule in the "horn" of Africa.		
Germany takes land in eastern and southwestern Africa.		

6. **Predict Consequences** According to the text, missionaries wanted to help Africans and thought that expanding Western influence into the interior of the continent would improve life for Africans. How do you think these missionaries would have reacted to King Leopold II's rule of the Congo?

7. **Draw Conclusions** Why did the British seek to claim Boer lands north of Cape Colony?

African Resistance: Text

8. **Identify Steps in a Process** What steps did Menelik II take to successfully resist Italian conquest?

9. **Draw Conclusions** How did Western education affect different members of the African elite?

Interactive Reading Notepad

The Age of Imperialism

Lesson 3 Europe in the Muslim World

Key Terms

Muhammad Ahmad	genocide
Mahdi	Muhammad Ali
pasha	concession
sultan	

Academic Vocabulary

bureaucracy: government staffed by administrators who follow rigid rules

intervening: becoming involved in events in order to have influence on outcome

output: yield

successor: the person who takes a position after another has left

Lesson Objectives

1 **Explain** how internal and external pressures shaped the Muslim world.

2 **Identify** the challenges facing the Ottoman empire and Persia.

3 **Describe** the ways Egypt tried to modernize, including the opening of the Suez Canal.

Unrest in Muslim Regions: Text

Identify Cause and Effect as you read "Unrest in Muslim Regions." Fill in a chart like this one below showing the causes of unrest in Muslim regions during the 1700s and 1800s.

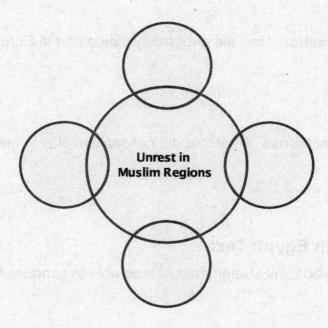

1. **Integrate Information from Diverse Sources** Read the first paragraph of "Unrest in Muslim Regions." Then look at the photo of the Battle of the Pyramids in Egypt. What different kinds of information about European contact with Muslim regions can you draw from both sources?

2. **Draw Inferences** Why would Muhammad Ahmad be especially effective at leading resistance against the British?

The Ottoman Empire Declines: Text

3. **Compare and Contrast** Compare and contrast the revolts against the Ottoman empire in Greece and Armenia.

4. **Analyze Information** How did geography play a part in European interest in Muslim regions?

5. **Identify Central Issues** What role did nationalism play in the Armenian genocide?

Modernization in Egypt: Text

6. **Infer** Why do you think Muhammad Ali was able to conquer Arabia, Syria, and Sudan?

7. **Analyze Interactions** Why did the Ottoman empire allow Britain to dictate policies in Egypt?

European Imperialism in Persia: Text

8. **Analyze Interactions** How did the reasons for Russia's and Britain's interest in Persia change?

9. **Draw Conclusions** Why might two groups of Persian nationalists have such different views on how Persia should respond to Western imperialism?

The Age of Imperialism

Lesson 4 India Becomes a British Colony

Key Terms

sati

sepoy

viceroy

deforestation

Ram Mohun Roy

purdah

Academic Vocabulary

overall: total

incorporate: join with something that already exists

distinctions: separations into different groups

Lesson Objectives

1 **Understand** the causes and effects of the Sepoy Rebellion.

2 **Explain** the impact of British rule on India.

3 **Describe** how the British and Indians viewed one another.

4 **Trace** the origins of Indian nationalism

The British East India Company: Text

Identify Cause and Effect As you read "The British East India Company," examine the text for clues that signal cause and effect. Then use a chart like this one to record major causes and effects of British colonial rule in India.

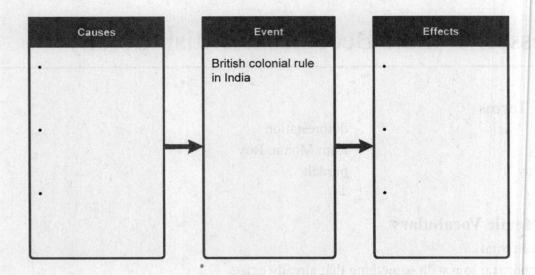

Causes	Event	Effects
•	British colonial rule in India	•
•		•
•		•

1. **Analyze Interactions** How did the British react to the diversity of the people in India?

2. **Summarize** What were some of the positive things that the British East India Company did in India?

3. **Analyze Interactions** How did a lack of cultural understanding contribute to the Sepoy Rebellion?

India Under British Rule: Text

4. **Vocabulary; Determine Meaning** Read the first sentence of the second paragraph. Look at the context of the word *overall* to determine its meaning. What would the *overall* British economy include?

5. **Draw Conclusions** Why would machine-made textiles from Britain ruin India's hand-weaving industry?

6. **Cite Evidence** from the text for the argument that India grew more unified under British rule.

Diverse Views on Culture: Text

7. **Cite Evidence** Why is Ram Mohun Roy called the founder of Indian nationalism? In what ways did he adopt Western culture?

8. **Hypothesize** What might have led the majority of British people to dismiss Indian culture so readily?

The Growth of Indian Nationalism: Text

9. **Compare and Contrast** the Muslim League to the Indian National Congress.

10. **Evaluate** Why did British imperialists think Western education would benefit both Indians and the British? In what way were they mistaken?

The Age of Imperialism

Lesson 5 China and the West

Key Terms

balance of trade

trade surplus

trade deficit

Opium War

indemnity

extraterritoriality

Taiping Rebellion

Sino-Japanese War

Open Door Policy

Guang Xu

Boxer Uprising

Sun Yixian

Academic Vocabulary

stipulate: to specifically demand something in an agreement

emphasis: particular attention

principle: value or belief

Lesson Objectives

1 **Describe** why and how Westernizers tried to gain trade rights in China.

2 **Explain** how reformers tried to strengthen China.

3 **Understand** why the Qing dynasty fell.

Economic Interest in China: Text

1. **Cite Evidence** Why was Britain eager to have China buy products from western countries as well as sell products to them?

2. **Identify Cause and Effect** As you read "Economic Interest in China," examine the text for clues that signal how British intervention affected China. Then use a chart like this one to record major effects.

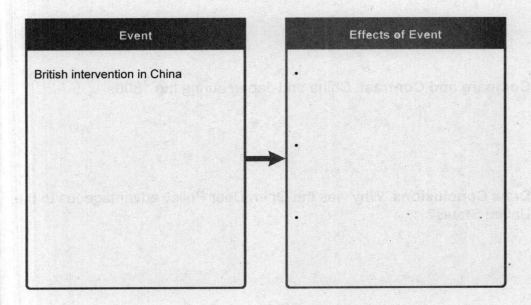

Event	Effects of Event
British intervention in China	•
	•
	•

3. **Identify Causes and Effects** What were the causes and effects of the Opium War?

The Taiping Rebellion and a Weakened China: Text

4. **Identify Supporting Details** What details under "The Taiping Rebellion and a Weakened China" support the idea that China was weaker when the rebellion took place than it had been in earlier times?

5. **Draw Inferences** Why do you think the Qing dynasty had to share power with regional commanders after the Taiping Rebellion?

Reform Efforts in China: Text

6. **Draw Conclusions** Why did the Chinese government refuse to support the self-strengthening movement?

7. **Compare and Contrast** China and Japan during the 1800s.

8. **Draw Conclusions** Why was the Open Door Policy advantageous to the United States?

The Fall of the Qing Dynasty: Text

9. **Summarize** What led to resentment of foreigners living in China in the late 1800s and early 1900s?

10. **Identify Causes and Effects** What were the effects of the Boxer Uprising?

The Age of Imperialism

Lesson 6 The Modernization of Japan

Key Terms

Matthew Perry	zaibatsu
Mutsuhito	homogeneous society
Tokyo	First Sino-Japanese War
Meiji Restoration	Russo-Japanese War
Diet	

Academic Vocabulary

emphasizing: stressing

thereby: by that means, because of that

Lesson Objectives

1 **Identify** the problems faced by Tokugawa Japan.

2 **Explain** how the United States opened Japan to the outside world.

3 **Analyze** the causes and effects of the Meiji Restoration.

4 **Describe** how Japan began to build an empire.

Unrest in Tokugawa Japan: Text

1. **Understand Main Ideas** Read the first three paragraphs of "Unrest in Tokugawa Japan." What does the text convey about this period in Japan?

2. **Identify Cause and Effect** As you read the lesson, examine the text for clues that signal cause and effect. Then use a chart like this one to record major causes and effects of the decline of Tokugawa Japan.

Decline of Tokugawa Japan

Causes of Decline	Effects of Decline
•	•
•	•
•	•

The Opening of Japan: Text

3. **Hypothesize** Why do you think the United States approached Japan in the way it did, *demanding* that Japan open the door to trade and diplomacy?

4. **Draw Conclusions** How did Japan's adaptation to Western ways help balance its relationship with Western countries?

Transformation during the Meiji Period: Text

5. **Compare and Contrast** Compare and contrast Japan before and during the Meiji Restoration.

6. **Cite Evidence** What evidence in the text supports the claim that Japan successfully updated its industries during the Meiji Restoration?

7. **Summarize** During the Meiji Restoration, many changes were made to the hierarchical class system in Japan. What inequalities remained?

Japan Builds an Empire: Text

8. **Compare and Contrast** how Japan and Korea dealt with imperialistic ambitions of other countries.

9. **Summarize** How did Japan gain rule over Korea?

Interactive Reading Notepad

The Age of Imperialism

Lesson 7 Southeast Asia and the Pacific

Key Terms

French Indochina   indigenous

Mongkut   penal colony

Spanish-American War   Maori

Liliuokalani

Academic Vocabulary

transition: passage from one way to another

Lesson Objectives

1 **Describe** how Europe and the United States built colonies in Southeast Asia.

2 **Explain** how imperialism spread to the islands of the Pacific.

3 **Analyze** how Australia and New Zealand achieved self-rule.

European Imperialism in Southeast Asia: Text

1. **Determine Central Ideas** What is the main reason the Dutch and British colonized areas of Southeast Asia? Cite evidence from the text to support your answer.

2. **Summarize** Read "The French in Indochina." What seems to be the main reason the French colonized Vietnam?

3. **Draw Inferences** How did the unequal treaties that Siam made with Western powers keep it independent and free from colonization?

Military Might and the Philippines: Text

4. **Integrate Information from Diverse Sources** Read the paragraphs about the Spanish-American War in "Military Might and the Philippines." Then look at the illustration showing the Battle of Manila Bay. What do the text and the illustration convey about the battle? Is the information in the picture and text consistent? In what ways?

5. **Identify Cause and Effect** As you read "Military Might and the Philippines," examine the text for clues that signal cause and effect. Then use a chart like this one to record major causes and effects of Western involvement in the nation. Focus on how the Filipino rebels felt about imperialism.

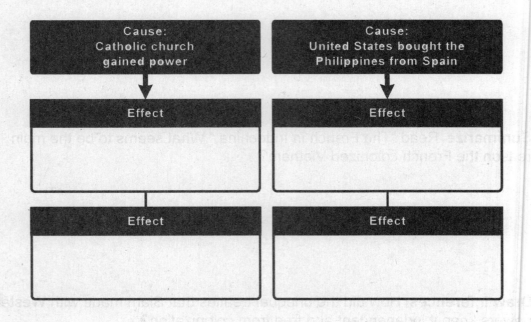

Strategic Holdings in the Pacific Islands: Text

6. **Summarize** Why were Western countries interested in the islands of the Pacific?

7. **Draw Inferences** Why did the Hawaiian queen Liliuokalani want to reduce the influence of foreigners, particularly American sugar growers?

Europeans in Australia: Text

8. **Cite Evidence** Who were the first groups of white settlers to Australia? How did they did they fare? Cite evidence from the text to support your answer.

9. **Identify Cause and Effect** Why did Australian colonies unite into a commonwealth? Why was this in Britain's best interest?

New Zealand's Story: Text

10. **Compare and Contrast** How was the experience of the Maori similar to and different from that of the Australian Aborigines when white settlers arrived?

11. **Draw Conclusions** Why did New Zealanders preserve close ties with the British empire?

The Age of Imperialism

Lesson 8 The Americas in the Age of Imperialism

Key Terms

regionalism	Monroe Doctrine
caudillo	Panama Canal
Benito Juárez	confederation
La Reforma	dominion
peonage	métis

Academic Vocabulary

compile: to put together from several sources

enlightened: educated, informed

tangible: real or concrete

Lesson Objectives

1 **Identify** the political problems faced by new Latin American nations.

2 **Describe** Mexico's struggle to achieve stability.

3 **Explain** why Latin America entered a cycle of economic dependence.

4 **Analyze** the influence of the United States on Latin America, including the opening of the Panama Canal.

5 **Analyze** how Canada achieved self-rule.

Political Problems Linger: Text

1. **Identify Cause and Effect** How did refrigerated ships change relationships between countries around the world?

2. **Hypothesize** How might Latin America have developed after colonialism if Simón Bolívar's dream had come true?

3. **Understand Main Ideas** Who were the caudillos? What do you think life was like under the caudillos?

4. **Summarize** Why did Latin American countries have a difficult time adopting democracy?

Mexico's Search for Stability: Text

5. **Identify Cause and Effect** What were some effects of the United States annexing Texas in 1845?

6. **Compare** Benito Juárez and General Porfirio Díaz were very different rulers. Regardless, both helped to stabilize Mexico. What did each do to help stabilize the country? What were the advances each made?

7. **Draw Inferences** Which ruler, Benito Juárez or General Porfirio Díaz, would Mexicans who lived in poverty have preferred? Why?

The Economics of Latin America's Dependence: Text

8. **Summarize** How did the policies of ruling governments policies prevent colonies from developing their own economies?

9. **Identify Cause and Effect** What were some positive effects of foreign investment in Latin America?

The United States Wields Power and Influence: Text

10. **Cite Evidence** What statement did the Monroe Doctrine make to the rest of the world? Cite evidence from the text to support your answer.

11. **Identify Cause and Effect** How did the United States grow as a result of the war with Mexico?

12. Draw Conclusions How did building the Panama Canal both help and hurt the United States? Has it been more beneficial or more problematic?

Canada Achieves Self-Rule: Text

13. Evaluate Information The text states that because Canadians shared language and cultural roots with Britain, they were able to achieve self-rule faster. Do you think this is true?

14. Analyze Sequence As you read "Canada Achieves Self-Rule," examine the text for the order of events. Then use a chart like this one to record major events that led to Canada's independence.

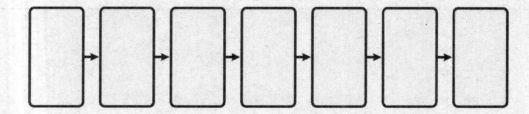

World War I and the Russian Revolution

Lesson 1 World War I Begins

Key Terms

entente
militarism
Alsace and Lorraine

ultimatum
mobilize
neutrality

Academic Vocabulary

status: high standing, rank, or prestige
overseas: across the sea; foreign

Lesson Objectives

1 **Describe** how imperialism, nationalism, and militarism pushed Europe closer to war.

2 **Identify** the key event that sparked World War I.

3 **Trace** how the alliance system drew nations into the war.

European Powers Form Alliances: Text

1. **Compare and Contrast** Read the two quotes from the text below.

> "The future belongs to peace."
>
> —French economist Frédéric Passy

> "I shall not live to see the Great War, but you will see it, and it will start in the east."
>
> German Chancellor Otto von Bismarck

What evidence supports each man's viewpoint?

2. **Cite Evidence** Why did the countries of Europe believe that alliances would guarantee peace? Use evidence from the text in your answer.

Major Causes of World War I: Text

3. **Vocabulary: Determine Meaning** Using context clues, determine the meaning of the term *arms race.*

4. **Identify Cause and Effect** How did imperialism lead to increased tension and stronger alliances?

5. **Make Inferences** Why did nationalist developments such as Pan-Slavism and the two Balkan Wars increase tensions to such a great degree?

The Balkan Powder Keg Explodes: Text

6. **Synthesize** Why did Austria-Hungary and Germany go to war against Serbia? Think about and include elements of the following in your answer:
   - nationalism
   - international rivalries
   - militarism

Interactive Reading Notepad • Lesson 1

The Alliance System Leads to War: Text

7. **Analyze Sequence** Use the graphic organizer below to create a time line. Fill in each box with the date that various nations went to war with each other. Then draw lines from each box to the correct point on the time line. Start your time line with the assassination of Archduke Francis Ferdinand. What conclusions can you draw from this time line?

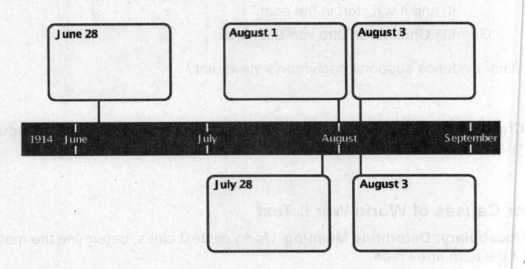

8. **Use Visual Information** Look at the map of European alliances in the text. Why did Germany fear an alliance between France and Russia?

9. **Draw Conclusions** Why were young men on both sides eager to fight when World War I started?

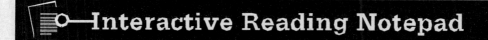

World War I and the Russian Revolution

Lesson 2 Fighting the Great War

Key Terms

stalemate

zeppelin

U-boat

convoy

Dardanelles

T. E. Lawrence

Academic Vocabulary

utilized: put to practical use

confronted: faced in opposition

Lesson Objectives

1 **Understand** how trench warfare led to a stalemate on the Western Front.

2 **Identify** and describe the impact of modern military technology on the fighting.

3 **Outline** the course of the war on multiple European fronts.

4 **Explain** how the war was a global conflict.

A New Kind of War: Text

1. **Draw Conclusions** Why did both sides dig trenches on the Western Front?

2. **Make Inferences** Why did trenches cause a stalemate on the Western Front?

3. **Analyze Style and Rhetoric** Re-read the quote from the text below. Why do you think Schmieder contrasted the noise of war with bird-song? What does the passage tell us about the people who fought the war?

> "The blue French cloth mingled with the German grey upon the ground, and in some places the bodies were piled so high that one could take cover from shell-fire behind them. The noise was so terrific that orders had to be shouted by each man into the ear of the next. And whenever there was a momentary lull in the tumult of battle and the groans of the wounded, one heard, high up in the blue sky, the joyful song of birds! Birds singing just as they do at home in spring-time! It was enough to tear the heart out of one's body!"

> —German soldier, Richard Schmieder writing from the trenches in France

Modern Military Technology: Text

4. **Summarize** Using the concept web graphic organizer, summarize the key technologies used in the war and their effects.

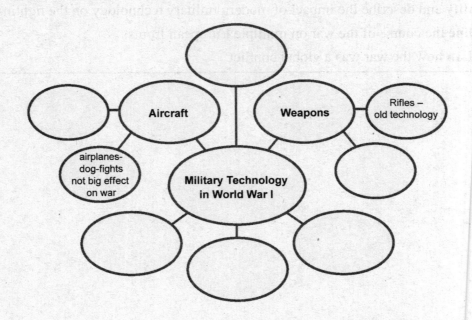

Interactive Reading Notepad • Lesson 2

5. **Draw Conclusions** Rank the new technologies from most important to least, and provide the reasoning for each ranking.

Other European Fronts: Text

6. **Make Inferences** Why were there such high casualties on the Eastern Front?

7. **Hypothesize** Did the battles in Italy and the Balkans have an impact on the outcome of the war? Why or why not?

A Global Conflict: Text

8. **Summarize** Explain the significance of the Dardanelles and what happened there.

9. **Cite Evidence** Why might some Turkish Armenians have helped the Russians during World War I? Cite evidence from the text to support your answer.

10. **Synthesize** What influence did the war in the Middle East have on the war as a whole?

11. **Hypothesize** Why did some people from the European colonies think that fighting in World War I might lead to citizenship or independence?

World War I and the Russian Revolution

Lesson 3 World War I Ends

Key Terms

total war	self-determination
conscription	armistice
contraband	pandemic
Lusitania	reparation
propaganda	radical
atrocity	collective security
Fourteen Points	mandate

Academic Vocabulary

eroded: ate into or wore away

widespread: occurring in many places

Lesson Objectives

1 **Describe** how World War I became a total war.

2 **Explain** how U.S. entry into the war led to an Allied victory.

3 **List** the effects of World War I in terms of financial costs, high casualty rates, and political impact.

4 **Describe** the issues at the Paris Peace Conference and the impact of Woodrow Wilson's Fourteen Points.

5 **Summarize** the terms and impact of the Treaty of Versailles.

Governments Direct Total War: Text

1. **Compare and Contrast** Read the two paragraphs under the heading "Blockades and Submarines Impact Economies." How did both Britain and Germany violate international law?

2. **Cite Evidence** In what ways did women's contributions and experiences during World War I directly contribute to social and political changes for women after the war?

Morale Breaks Down: Text

3. **Identify Cause and Effect** What impact did the Russian Revolution have on the Allied war effort in Europe?

The United States Enters the War: Text

4. **Draw Conclusions** President Wilson described World War I as a "war to end war." What efforts did he make to deliver on that promise?

5. **Determine Central Ideas** Why did the Germans launch a major offensive in in early 1918? Why did the offensive ultimately fail?

The Great War Ends: Text

6. **Analyze Interactions Among Events** Uprisings by hungry people in cities across Germany contributed to Kaiser William's decision to step down in September 1918. What events together caused widespread hunger in Germany?

7. **Analyze Data** Using data in the infographic "The Costs of World War I," describe how American financial costs and casualties compared to the costs and casualties borne by the other Allies. How can you explain these differences?

8. **Determine Central Ideas** Why were conditions immediately following the war ripe for rebellion and revolution?

Making the Peace: Text

9. **Analyze a Political Cartoon** In the political cartoon the dove replies, "Of course I want to please everybody but isn't this a bit thick? How does this statement reflect how the U.S. Senate felt about the League of Nations?

10. In what ways was Germany forced to make amends for the outbreak of World War I?

Effects of the Peace Settlements: Text

11. **Integrate Information from Diverse Sources** The fifth of Wilson's Fourteen Points states: "Impartial adjustment of colonial claims based on interests of governments and native populations." Read the two paragraphs in the section "The Mandate System." Do you think the Allies followed Wilson's recommendation for dealing with colonial holdings? Why or why not?

World War I and the Russian Revolution

Lesson 4 Revolution in Russia

Key Terms
proletariat
soviet
V.I. Lenin

Cheka
commissar

Academic Vocabulary
crucial: of vital importance
withdrawal: the act of leaving

Lesson Objectives

1 **Explain** the causes of the (February) March Revolution.

2 **Describe** the goals of Lenin and the Bolsheviks in the October Revolution.

3 **Summarize** the outcome of the civil war in Russia.

4 **Analyze** how Lenin built a Communist state in the Soviet Union.

Causes of the February Revolution: Text

1. **Distinguish Between Fact and Opinion** Tsarina Alexandra once confided to a friend, "They are constantly frightening the emperor with threats of revolution, and here,—you see it yourself—we need merely to show ourselves and at once their hearts are ours." Was the tsarina expressing fact, opinion, or a combination of both? Cite evidence from the text to support your response.

2. **Identify Cause and Effect** How was World War I a major cause of revolution in Russia? Provide specific details from the text to support your answer.

3. **Analyze Interactions Among Ideas** According to Marxism, the proletariat would overthrow governments and set up a classless society in which wealth and power would be equally shared. Did Lenin's version of Marxism remain true to the spirit of Marxism? Why or why not?

Lenin Leads the Bolsheviks: Text

4. **Identify Cause and Effect** How did the Bolsheviks gain power and momentum?

The October Revolution Brings the Bolsheviks to Power: Text

5. **Identify Cause and Effect** How did the actions and inactions of the Russian provisional government cause the October Revolution?

6. **Draw Inferences** Based on the text's description, do you think the provisional government forces strongly opposed the Bolsheviks' revolution? Explain your reasoning. Why do you think the government forces responded in the way they did?

7. **Draw Conclusions** Why was Lenin's promise of "Peace, Land, and Bread" so effective in gaining support for the Bolsheviks? Did Lenin fulfill his promise to the Russian people? Cite evidence from the text to support your answer.

Civil War Erupts in Russia: Text

8. **Determine Author's Purpose** Examine the poster "For a United Russia. France liberated." Using what you know about the opposing forces in the Russian civil war, what was the purpose of this poster? How does the poster use imagery to achieve its purpose?

9. **Identify Cause and Effect** What were the causes and effects of Allied intervention in the Russian Civil War?

10. **Analyze Interactions** How were the Reds able to defeat the Whites in the Russian Civil War?

The Communist Soviet Union Emerges: Text

11. **Assess an Argument** The Communists drew up a constitution that, according to the text, asserted that "all political power, resources, and means of production would belong to workers and peasants." How truthful was this assertion? How do you think this affected the credibility of the Soviet Union?

12. **Compare and Contrast** How were war communism and the New Economic Policy different in their policies and their results?

13. **Determine Meaning** In the last paragraph of this text, Lenin's concerns about Stalin are revealed through Lenin's own words. In the context of this quotation, what do you think Lenin meant by the phrase "sufficient caution"?

The World Between the Wars

Lesson 1 Revolution and Nationalism in Latin America

Key Terms

Porfirio Díaz
hacienda
Emiliano Zapata
Venustiano Carranza
nationalization

Lázaro Cárdenas
economic nationalism
cultural nationalism
Good Neighbor Policy

Academic Vocabulary

assets: things of value
intervening: coming between two arguing factions

Lesson Objectives

1 **Identify** causes and effects of the Mexican Revolution.

2 **Analyze** the effects of economic and political nationalism on Latin America.

3 **Trace** the changing relationship between Latin America and the United States.

The Mexican Revolution: Text

1. **Identify Cause and Effect** Describe at least three reasons people supported the Mexican Revolution.

2. **Infer** Why was dictator Porfirio Díaz elected president so many times? What finally made people turn against him and demand changes to the government?

3. **Identify Cause and Effect** Why did Victoriano Huerta and other rebels force Francisco Madero to resign?

4. **Draw Conclusions** Why did Venustiano Carranza turn on his allies Emiliano Zapata and Franciso "Pancho" Villa?

Economic and Social Reform: Text

5. **Summarize** What were the main provisions of the Mexican Constitution of 1917?

6. **Draw Conclusions** Why was land distribution such a key issue in Mexico?

Interactive Reading Notepad • Lesson 1

Nationalism Spreads in Latin America: Text

7. **Identify Cause and Effect** How did the Great Depression affect Latin America?

8. **Analyze Interactions** How did Latin American writers, artists, and thinkers react to events during the 1920s?

9. **Identify Central Issues** In what ways did Franklin Roosevelt change the policy of the United States toward Latin America? Provide examples from the text.

The World Between the Wars

Lesson 2 Nationalist Movements in Africa and the Middle East

Key Terms

apartheid	Atatürk
Pan-Africanism	Reza Khan
Marcus Garvey	Pan-Arabism
négritude movement	Balfour Declaration
Asia Minor	

Academic Vocabulary

assert: maintain or defend

advocated: supported or favored

Lesson Objectives

1 **Explain** how Africans resisted colonial rule.

2 **Describe** the rise of nationalism in Africa.

3 **Describe** how Turkey and Persia modernized.

4 **Understand** how the mandate systems contributed to Arab nationalism and to conflict between Jews and Arabs.

Africans Protest Colonial Rule: Text

1. **Summarize** How did the European governments treat black Africans in Kenya and Rhodesia? Why did the governments act this way? Cite evidence from the text.

2. **Identify Cause and Effect** What role did the ANC play in South Africa? What was the effect of its actions?

A Rising Tide of African Nationalism: Text

3. **Identify Cause and Effect** What was the Pan-African Congress? How effective was it? Explain.

4. **Draw Conclusions** How did some writers in West Africa and the Caribbean create a sense of pride among Africans? How might their work have affected readers outside Africa?

5. **Identify Supporting Details** Why did the British government grant Egypt independence in 1922?

Modernization of Turkey and Persia: Text

Compare Complete the graphic organizer to compare the rule of Atatürk and Reza Khan.

Leader/Nation	Business/Economy	Law/Government	Society
Reza Khan/Persia (Iran)			
Atatürk/Turkey			

6. **Identify Cause and Effect** Why did a nationalist movement grow in Persia after World War I?

Nationalism and Conflict in the Middle East: Text

7. **Identify Cause and Effect** Why did foreign companies begin to move to the Middle East after World War I? How did Arab nationalists respond?

8. **Summarize** How did the Treaty of Versailles impact the Middle East? Cite examples from the narrative.

9. **Synthesize** What promise did the Allies make to Arabs in the Palestine Mandate? How did it conflict with the Balfour Declaration? What was the result of these actions? Cite evidence from the text.

Interactive Reading Notepad • Lesson 2

The World Between the Wars

Lesson 3 India Seeks Self-Rule

Key Terms

Mohandas Gandhi   civil disobedience

Amritsar massacre   untouchable

ahimsa   boycott

Academic Vocabulary

discriminate: to treat differently because of prejudice

Lesson Objectives

1 **Explain** the impact of World War I and the Amritsar massacre on Indian nationalism.

2 **Evaluate** the ideas of Mohandas Gandhi.

3 **Analyze** how Gandhi led resistance to political oppression in India.

India's Struggle for Independence Begins: Text

1. **Identify Supporting Details** How was Gandhi treated when he returned to India. Why?

Analyze Sequence Complete the graphic organizer to show how World War I started a chain of events that led to the Congress party's call for independence.

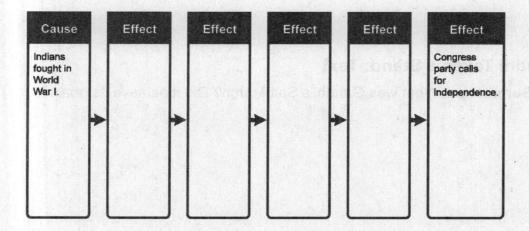

Cause	Effect	Effect	Effect	Effect	Effect
Indians fought in World War I.					Congress party calls for independence.

2. **Identify Cause and Effect** What were the Rowlatt Acts? What effect did they have on the nationalist movement?

Gandhi's Philosophy of Civil Disobedience: Text

3. **Summarize** Summarize Gandhi's main beliefs.

4. **Check Understanding** How did Gandhi apply Henry David Thoreau's idea about civil disobedience to India's political situation?

Gandhi Takes a Stand: Text

5. **Summarize** What was Gandhi's Salt March? Did it achieve its goals?

6. **Evaluate Explanations** What reasons did the British government give for postponing independence during the late 1930s? What was the effect of this decision?

The World Between the Wars

Lesson 4 New Forces in China and Japan

Key Terms

Twenty-One Demands

May Fourth Movement

vanguard

Guomindang

Jiang Jieshi

Mao Zedong

Long March

ultranationalist

Manchuria

Hirohito

Academic Vocabulary

intellectual: involving the ability to reason or think clearly

faction: a group within a larger group

manipulated: influenced skillfully, often unfairly

Lesson Objectives

1 **Explain** the key challenges faced by the Chinese republic in the early 1900s.

2 **Analyze** the struggle between nationalists and communists in China.

3 **Summarize** the effects of liberal changes in Japan in the 1920s.

4 **Describe** the rise of extreme nationalism and militarism in Japan.

5 **Describe** the impact of the Japanese invasion of China.

Trouble in the Chinese Republic: Text

As you read "Trouble in the Chinese Republic," complete the following chart by listing the multiple causes of upheaval in the Chinese republic.

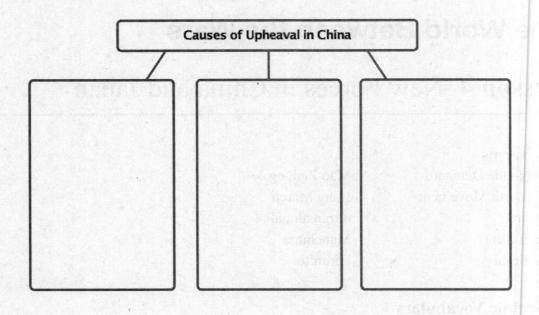

1. **Identify Cause and Effect** What were two responses of the Chinese people to the country's problems?

2. **Support Ideas with Evidence** How did warlord uprisings and foreign imperialism lead to the May Fourth Movement?

3. **Summarize** Why did China give in to some of the Twenty-One Demands?

Nationalists and Communists: Text

4. **Draw Conclusions** Who was defeated during the Northern Expedition? Why was this significant?

5. **Identify Cause and Effect** How did the Long March contribute to the rise of communism in China?

6. **Analyze Maps** Look at the route of the Long March as shown on the map "Civil War in China". What natural features made the Long March difficult?

China Faces Japanese Imperialism: Text

7. **Draw Conclusions** The leader of a faction within the Guomindang kidnapped Jiang and held him until he agreed to ally with the Communists against the Japanese. Why would this leader take such a drastic step?

8. **Summarize** What was the "Rape of Nanjing"?

9. **Contrast** Marxism was based on the rise of the proletariat, or industrial working class. How was Chinese communism different from classic Marxism?

Conflicting Forces in Japan: Text

10. Cite Evidence What were some sources of unrest in Japan during the 1920s?

11. Draw Conclusions How did Japan grow into a major economic and imperial power during and immediately after World War I?

12. Identify Central Issues Why did Japan want to expand its territories during and after World War I?

The Ultranationalist Reaction: Text

13. Identify Supporting Details What were some of the reasons for the ultranationalists' discontent during the 1930s?

14. Identify Cause and Effect Summarize the causes and effects of the Manchurian incident.

Militarists Gain Power: Text

15. Infer Why did militarists and ultranationalists glorify Hirohito and encourage the revival of traditional values?

16. Generate Explanations How did the government react to the demands of the ultranationalists?

17. Identify Supporting Details What is one example of Japan's continued refusal to cooperate internationally? What is one example of Japan's continued course of expansion overseas during the 1930s?

The World Between the Wars

Lesson 5 The West After World War I

Key Terms

flapper	Maginot Line
Miriam Ferguson	Kellogg-Briand Pact
Prohibition	disarmament
Marie Curie	general strike
Albert Einstein	overproduction
Harlem Renaissance	finance
psychoanalysis	Federal Reserve
abstract art	Great Depression
dada	Franklin D. Roosevelt
surrealism	New Deal

Academic Vocabulary

emancipation: freedom from restrictions

spontaneously: caused by inner forces, self-generated

suppressed: put down by force, subdued

affluent: rich, wealthy

Lesson Objectives

1 **Analyze** how Western society and culture changed after World War I.

2 **Identify** the contributions of modern scientists such as Marie Curie and Albert Einstein.

3 **Summarize** the domestic and foreign policy issues that the Western democracies faced after World War I.

4 **Describe** how the global depression began and spread.

5 **Explain** the responses of Britain, France, and the United States to the Great Depression.

Social Change After World War I: Text

1. **Identify Cause and Effect** What were some of the new technological innovations that were developed after World War I? How did they affect the Western world?

2. **Make Generalizations** How did flappers symbolize women's emancipation in the Jazz Age?

Scientific Discoveries: Text

3. **Summarize** Why did Curie's and Einstein's theories unsettle the general public?

4. **Sequence Events** How did Freud's work have an impact beyond medicine?

Literature Reflects New Perspectives: Text

5. **Draw Conclusions** Describe the "Lost Generation" of authors. How does the label *lost* apply to the themes they explored in their work?

6. **Identify Supporting Details** Describe the "stream of consciousness" literary style.

Modern Art and Architecture: Text

7. **Determine Point of View** Why did critics call the new artists "fauves", or wild beasts?

8. **Compare** What did surrealism have in common with the stream-of-consciousness technique and Freud's work?

9. **Summarize** In one or two sentences, summarize the ways in which Dadaists and surrealists each reflected a new worldview.

Postwar Politics in the West: Text

10. **Compare and Contrast** Compare unrest in Britain, France, and the United States during the 1920s. What problems did France and Britain share? What caused unrest in the United States?

11. **Identify Cause and Effect** What was one of the causes of social unrest and the popularization of radical ideas in the West? Explain your answer.

International Relations: Text

12. Identify Cause and Effect Why did the French build the Maginot Line?

13. Analyze Interactions How did the British government feel about the conditions set out in the Treaty of Versailles?

14. Determine Central Ideas What was one of the weaknesses of the League of Nations?

Economics in the Postwar Era: Text

15. Summarize Describe the economic condition of Britain after World War I.

16. Identify Key Ideas How did the United States aid the economic recovery in Europe after World War I?

17. **Compare and Contrast** How did the postwar economic recovery differ in Britain and France?

The Great Depression: Text

18. **Identify Cause and Effect** Explain how the fall in demand for raw materials and agricultural products contributed to the Great Depression.

19. **Sequence Events** How did the beginning of the Great Depression in the United States affect world markets?

Western Democracies React to the Depression: Text

20. **Evaluate Arguments** Was the New Deal successful? Explain.

21. **Determine Central Issues** How did the British government respond to the Great Depression?

22. **Identify Cause and Effect** How did the Federal Reserve Board contribute to the outbreak of the Great Depression?

The World Between the Wars

Lesson 6 Fascism Emerges in Italy

Key Terms

Benito Mussolini

Black Shirt

March on Rome

totalitarian state

fascism

Academic Vocabulary

proclaimed: announced officially

ideology: a system of ideas that guides an individual, movement, or political program

---

Lesson Objectives

1 **Describe** the rise of Mussolini.

2 **Summarize** Mussolini's policies as leader of Italy.

3 **Identify** the characteristics of totalitarianism and fascism.

The Rise of Mussolini: Text

As you read "The Rise of Mussolini" and "Mussolini's Totalitarian Rule," complete the flow chart below by identifying the main ideas and events under each heading.

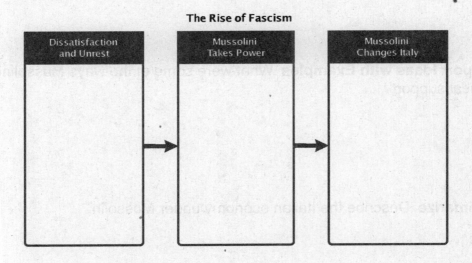

The Rise of Fascism

| Dissatisfaction and Unrest | Mussolini Takes Power | Mussolini Changes Italy |

1. **Identify Central Issues** What were postwar conditions like in Italy?

2. **Summarize** How did Mussolini come to power?

3. **Generate Explanations** Explain why you think people found Mussolini appealing.

Interactive Reading Notepad • Lesson 6

Mussolini's Totalitarian Rule: Text

4. Make Generalizations What was Fascist policy regarding children?

5. Support Ideas with Examples What were some of the ways Mussolini won political support?

6. Summarize Describe the Italian economy under Mussolini.

Characteristics of Fascism: Text

7. Identify Supporting Details Describe some basic features common to all forms of fascism.

8. Analyze Interactions How did Fascists view democracy?

9. Sequence Events How did the reaction of the West to Mussolini's government change over time?

The World Between the Wars

Lesson 7 The Soviet Union Under Stalin

Key Terms

command economy

collective

kulak

Gulag

socialist realism

Osip Mandelstam

Boris Pasternak

russification

atheism

Comintern

Academic Vocabulary

conform: to obey a set of standards

access: the ability to get and use

Lesson Objectives

1 **Explain** how Stalin built a command economy in the Soviet Union.

2 **Describe** how Stalin used terror to build a totalitarian state.

3 **Analyze** Stalin's use of propaganda to control thought and the arts.

4 **Summarize** the characteristics of Soviet society under Stalin.

5 **Understand** the goals of Soviet foreign policy.

Stalin Builds a Command Economy: Text

1. **Identify Central Ideas** What are some of the differences between a command economy and a capitalist economy?

2. **Generate Explanations** Why did some peasants resist the collectivization plan? How did Stalin respond to the peasant resistance of collectivization?

Control Through Terror: Text

3. **Summarize** What was the Great Purge? How did the purges increase Stalin's power?

4. **Draw Conclusions** How do you think Stalin's policies of terror affected the people of the Soviet Union and their feelings toward their government?

Stalin Builds a Totalitarian State: Text

5. **Support Ideas with Evidence** Describe some of the ways Stalin controlled cultural life in the Soviet Union.

6. **Draw Conclusions** How do you think people reacted to the policy of russification?

7. **Summarize** How did the treatment of artists and writers change under Stalin's rule?

Soviet Society Under Stalin: Text

8. Use Context Clues Using your own words, describe what the word *elite* means.

9. Draw Conclusions Who do you think made up the elite in Soviet society? How were these people treated differently from the rest of the Russian population?

10. Identify Main Ideas Why were state-run schools important to Stalin's communist goals?

Soviet Foreign Policy: Text

11. Draw Conclusions Why were Western nations wary of the Comintern?

12. Compare Describe the similarities in the foreign policy goals of Lenin and Stalin.

13. Support Ideas with Examples What progress did the Soviet Union make toward the goal of winning the support of other nations?

The World Between the Wars

Lesson 8 The Rise of Nazi Germany

Key Terms

chancellor

Ruhr Valley

hyperinflation

Adolf Hitler

Third Reich

Gestapo

Nuremberg Laws

Academic Vocabulary

passive: not active; nonviolent

regime: a government in power

Lesson Objectives

1 **Summarize** the political and economic problems faced by the Weimar Republic.

2 **Analyze** Hitler's rise to power.

3 **Describe** the political, social, economic, and cultural policies of Nazi Germany.

4 **Explain** why Eastern Europe turned to authoritarian rule.

The Weimar Republic: Reading

1. **Draw Conclusions** Which factor do you think might have been most significant in Hitler's rise to power? Explain your answer.

2. **Infer** Why do you think culture flourished in the Weimar Republic despite the government's problems?

Hitler Leads the Nazi Party: Reading

3. **Determine Central Ideas** How did Hitler shift political thought in Weimar Germany? Why did his radical ideas gain the support of many Germans?

4. **Explain an Argument** Explain Nazi ideology as depicted in Hitler's book *Mein Kampf*.

Interactive Reading Notepad • Lesson 8

The Third Reich: Reading

5. **Analyze Interactions** How did Hitler expand his control over the German people?

6. **Summarize** How did Hitler's anti-Semitism increase over time?

Authoritarian Rule in Eastern Europe: Reading

7. **Compare** Identify two ways that dictators from other Eastern European countries were similar to Hitler.

8. **Infer** How did World War I impact the rise of authoritarian rule in Eastern Europe?

Interactive Reading Notepad • Lesson 8

World War II

Lesson 1 Aggression, Appeasement, and War

Key Terms

appeasement

pacifism

Neutrality Acts

Axis Powers

Francisco Franco

Anschluss

Sudetenland

Nazi-Soviet Pact

Academic Vocabulary

sanctions: penalty

technology: scientific advances applied to practical purposes

---

Lesson Objectives

1 **Describe** how the Western democracies responded to aggression.

2 **Explain** the significance of the Spanish Civil War.

3 **Understand** how German aggression led Europe into World War II.

A Pattern of Aggression: Reading

1. **Summarize** Use the table below to sequence the acts of aggression.

Acts of Aggression	
Japan	
Italy	
Germany	

2. **Draw Inferences** How effective was the League of Nations in 1930? Give details from the reading to support your answer.

3. **Determine Central Ideas** Why did Germany, Italy, and Japan reach an agreement to form the Axis Powers?

The Spanish Civil War: Reading

4. **Determine Central Ideas** How was the Spanish Civil War another step in the march towards World War II?

German Aggression Continues: Reading

5. **Summarize** Use the table below to sequence German acts of aggression.

German Aggression	
March 1938	
Sept 1938	
March 1939	
Sept 1939	

6. **Determine Central Ideas** Why did Britons and other people in Western Europe have mixed feelings about the Munich Agreement?

World War II Begins: Reading

7. **Draw Inferences** Why did the democracies finally promise to protect Poland from a German invasion?

8. **Determine Central Ideas** How did the Nazi-Soviet Pact influence Hitler's decision to invade Poland?

World War II

Lesson 2 Axis Powers Advance

Key Terms

blitzkrieg   Erwin Rommel

Luftwaffe   Lend-Lease Act

Dunkirk   Atlantic Charter

Vichy   Hideki Tojo

Academic Vocabulary

available: ready for use; at hand

nullified: made invalid

Lesson Objectives

1 **Trace the** course of German aggression and British resistance in Europe.

2 **Describe** the Nazi invasion of the Soviet Union.

3 **Explain** how Japanese imperialism and the attack on Pearl Harbor brought the United States into the war.

Axis Domination of Europe: Text

1. **Summarize** How did the Axis Powers achieve victories in 1939 and 1940?

2. **Infer** Why do you think the air strike was important to Germany's plan to invade Britain?

3. **Identify Central Ideas** Explain the importance of Winston Churchill during World War II.

Nazis Attack the Soviet Union: Text

4. **Identify Cause and Effect** How did Hitler's invasion of the Soviet Union affect the Nazi-Soviet Pact?

5. **Draw Conclusions** How did Hitler's invasion of the Soviet Union work against him?

U.S. Involvement in the War: Text

6. **Summarize** Explain the sequence of events that led to U.S. entry into World War II.

7. **Compare** How was the Japanese attack on the U.S naval base at Pearl Harbor similar to the German invasion of Poland?

World War II

Lesson 3 The Holocaust

Key Terms

concentration camp

crematorium

Holocaust

Auschwitz

Academic Vocabulary

genocide: the deliberate killing of people who belong to a particular racial, political, or social group

liberated: set free

Lesson Objectives

1 **Identify** the roots of Nazi persecution of the Jews.

2 **Describe** how the Nazis carried out a program of genocide.

3 **Describe** the various acts of Jewish resistance.

4 **Summarize** the response of the Allies to the Holocaust.

The Nazi Campaign Against the Jews: Text

1. **Summarize** How did the Nazis use the concentration camp system throughout World War II?

2. **Determine Central Ideas** How did the Nazis put their anti-Semitic beliefs into practice?

3. **Draw Conclusions** Do you think the guilt of Hitler and the few who devised the "Final Solution" lessens the guilt of the many people who carried out those orders? Explain your answer.

4. **Contrast** How were death camps different from concentration camps? Which of Hitler's goals did the death camps address?

Jewish Resistance: Text

5. **Determine Central Ideas** Why was it difficult for non-Jewish civilians to help, hide, or protect their Jewish neighbors?

6. **Draw Inferences** How were Warsaw Ghetto residents an inspiration to others?

The Allies Respond to the Holocaust: Text

7. **Summarize** Why did the Allies take only limited action to protect the Jewish people in occupied Europe?

8. **Draw Inferences** After liberation, why was life difficult for European Jews who survived the Holocaust?

World War II

Lesson 4 The Allies Turn the Tide

Key Terms

internment	Joseph Stalin
Rosie the Riveter	Dwight Eisenhower
aircraft carrier	Stalingrad
Franklin Delano Roosevelt	D-Day
Winston Churchill	Yalta Conference

Academic Vocabulary

incessant: uninterrupted, ceaseless

inevitable: unavoidable; inescapable

Lesson Objectives

1 **Understand** how nations committed all of their resources to fighting World War II.

2 **Explain** how the Allies began to push back the Axis powers in Europe and the Pacific.

3 **Describe** the Normandy landings and the Allied advance toward Germany.

A Commitment to Total War: Text

1. **Integrate Information** Review the text concerning the Allies' war resources, and then look at the infographic showing the GDP for each country and the amount spent on certain resources for the war effort. Compare the two categories for each country. What do the text and the infographic show in terms of GDP of each country during the period 1939–1945 versus the Allied production of tanks and airplanes for the war effort?

2. **Summarize** How was business restructured on the Allied home fronts in order to support the war effort?

Progress on Three Fronts: Text

3. **Draw Inferences** Why was Hitler's strategic decision to try to take over the oil fields of the Soviet Union a disaster? Use details from the text to support your answer.

4. **Summarize** Fill in the graphic organizer titled, "Three Main Fronts of World War II, 1942–1943." There are three rows labeled Pacific, North Africa and Italy, and the Soviet Union. Using the text, list in each row the Allied and Axis leaders who were responsible for making the decisions on each front. Then, in one or two sentences, list turning points on each of the fronts during the war.

Three Main Fronts of World War II, 1942–1943		
	Leaders	Turning Point Soviet Union
Pacific		
North Africa and Italy		
Soviet Union		

A Second Front in Europe: Text

5. **Identify Steps in a Process** In order to pave the way for the invasion of D-Day, what preliminary steps did Eisenhower take on the Western Front to distract and weaken Germany? View the Flipbook of the B-24 bomber to support your answer.

6. **Identify Central Ideas** Using the pictures in the text and the narrative, provide a synopsis of what took place on the beaches of Normandy on D-Day and why it was so important for the Allies to succeed in this offensive.

World War II

Lesson 5 Victory for the Allies

Key Terms

Harry Truman	Manhattan Project
V-E Day	Harry Truman
Bataan Death March	Hiroshima
"island-hopping"	Nagasaki
Douglas MacArthur	Nuremberg Trials
kamikaze	United Nations (UN)

Academic Vocabulary

objective: something worked toward; a goal

convened: met; assembled

Lesson Objectives

1 **Understand** the reasons for the final defeat of the Nazis.

2 **Describe** how the Allies began to push back the Japanese in the Pacific.

3 **Explain** how the dropping of the atomic bombs ended the war.

4 **Describe** the aftermath of World War II and the founding of the United Nations.

End of the War in Europe: Text

1. **Use Visual Information** Review the text and the photograph of the soldiers at the Elbe River. What is significant about shaking of hands by American and Soviet soldiers at this point in the war?

2. **Summarize** Hitler and Germany faced major challenges toward the end of the war. Using the graphic organizer below, fill in information about each fact or event that describes why it was a major challenge for Germany.

Fact or Event	Challenge
Battle of Stalingrad	
Germany's location	
U.S. military production	

Battles in the Pacific: Text

3. **Paraphrase** Military operations in the Pacific theater were based on Allied collaboration, but operations were commanded by the U.S. Army, Navy, and Air Force. How did each contribute to Japan's defeat?

4. **Draw Inferences** Why was the victory at Guadalcanal a turning point in the war in the Pacific?

End of the War in the Pacific: Text

5. **Draw Conclusions** Why was the United States interested in developing a weapon of mass destruction?

6. **Assess an Argument** What were the general arguments for and against using atomic bombs to end World War II? List on one side reasons why Truman might have decided to use the atomic bomb, and on the other, reasons against using the weapon.

Use the Atomic Bomb	Do Not Use the Atomic Bomb

Aftermath of the War: Text

7. **Draw Inferences** What financial costs do you think the Axis should have been responsible for, and why?

8. **Identify Cause and Effect** The atrocities of the Nazis continued until the Allies liberated Europe and the death camps. Why do you believe it took an Allied military victory to stop the Nazis? Why didn't the German people end the Nazis' reign of terror?

9. **Identify Key Steps in a Process** After winning World War II, the Allies wanted to ensure that Axis countries would not threaten peace once again. Make a list of steps the Allies took to guard against a rebirth of Axis aggression.

The United Nations Is Formed: Text

10. **Summarize** Why was the United Nations created when there was already an organization, the League of Nations, designed to prevent world aggression?

Interactive Reading Notepad • Lesson 5

The Cold War Era

Lesson 1 A New Global Conflict

Key Terms

superpower	Warsaw Pact
Cold War	détente
Truman Doctrine	Fidel Castro
containment	John F. Kennedy
Marshall Plan	ideology
North Atlantic Treaty	Nikita Khrushchev
Organization (NATO)	Leonid Brezhnev

Academic Vocabulary

invoked: resorted to; called upon

comprised: was made up of

Lesson Objectives

1 **Summarize** how the outcome of World War II contributed to the development of the Cold War.

2 **Identify** continuing Cold War conflicts in Germany and Eastern Europe.

3 **Explain** the growth of the nuclear arms race.

4 **Analyze** how the Cold War became a global conflict.

5 **Compare** the United States and the Soviet Union in the Cold War.

Wartime Alliance Breaks Apart: Text

1. **Analyze Word Choices** What does *cold* in the term *Cold War* mean?

2. **Determine Central Ideas** How did Stalin make sure that the eastern part of Europe came under Soviet influence?

Soviet Aggression Grows: Text

3. **Analyze Word Choices** Why did Churchill call the divide between East and West the "Iron Curtain"? Explain the symbolism of both *iron* and *curtain*.

4. **Cite Evidence** How did the Truman Doctrine contain the communist threat in Greece?

5. **Sequence** List the sequence of events that led to the Berlin Airlift.

6. **Use Visual Information** Look at the map of divided Germany. How did the Soviets cut off supplies to West Berlin?

Interactive Reading Notepad • Lesson 1

Two Opposing Sides in Europe: Text

7. **Use Visual Information** Locate East Germany, Hungary, and Czechoslovakia on the map. Why did conflicts appear in these locations?

8. **Identify Supporting Details** In the graphic organizer below, list the different ways in which Eastern Europeans reacted against Soviet domination and how the Soviets responded to their actions.

East Germany (1953)	Hungary (1956)	Czechoslovakia (1968)
Reaction	Reaction	Reaction
Soviet Response	Soviet Response	Soviet Response

The Nuclear Arms Race: Text

9. **Assess an Argument** How did Mutually Assured Destruction (MAD) help prevent nuclear attacks?

10. **Compare and Contrast** Use the information in the infographic to answer this question: Why was the SALT II Treaty stronger than the Nuclear Test Ban Treaty?

11. **Explain Argument** Why did the United States and the Soviet Union reach a détente?

The Cold War Around the World: Text

12. **Analyze Word Choices** What does the heading "Where the Cold War Got Hot" mean?

13. **Use Visual Information** In the graphic organizer below, identify the Cold War "hotspots" by region.

Central America	Middle East	East Asia	Africa

14. **Cite Examples** In what country did communists come to power in 1959 and why?

Interactive Reading Notepad • Lesson 1

The Soviet Union During the Cold War: Text

15. Compare and Contrast In the graphic organizer below, list the similarities and differences between the experiences of Andrey Sakharov and Aleksandr Solzhenitsyn.

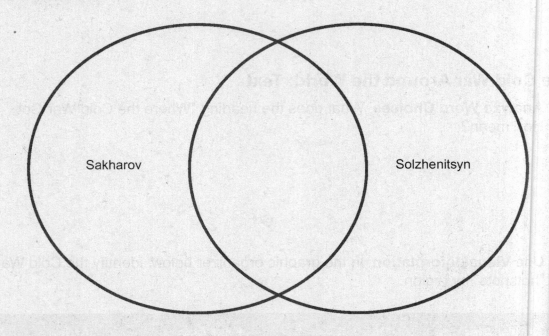

Sakharov

Solzhenitsyn

The United States in the Cold War: Text

16. Cite Examples In a market economy, which decisions are left to individuals?

17. Draw Inferences What are the benefits of a market economy?

The Cold War Era

Lesson 2 The Western Democracies and Japan

Key Terms

suburbanization

interdependence

recession

segregation

discrimination

Dr. Martin Luther King, Jr.

Konrad Adenauer

welfare state

Margaret Thatcher

European Union

gross domestic product (GDP)

Academic Vocabulary

prospered: succeeded, thrived, did well

Lesson Objectives

1 **Analyze** the postwar American Economy.

2 **Identify** developments in American society and government.

3 **Explain** how Western Europe rebuilt and moved toward greater unity.

4 **Describe** how Japan changed after World War II.

Postwar Prosperity in the United States: Text

1. **Cite Evidence** Give some examples of the new role played by the United States in the world after World War II.

2. **Draw Inferences** Why did Americans begin moving to the suburbs in the 1950s and 1960s?

3. **Identify Cause and Effect** What economic factors caused the economic recession in 1974?

The United States Responds to New Challenges: Text

4. **Determine Meaning** What is the difference between discrimination and segregation?

5. **Cite Evidence** In what ways were minorities denied equality and opportunity in the United States?

6. **Summarize** Why did the deficit soar in the 1980s?

7. **Using Visual Information** Look at the chart of military spending in the United States. By how much did military spending increase from 1980 to 1990?

Rebuilding Western Europe: Text

8. **Draw Inferences** Why did the United States rebuild West Germany after World War II?

9. **Categorize** Based on the infographic, what types of items were more expensive in East Germany?

10. **Cite Evidence** Give examples of goods that were less expensive in East Germany.

11. **Categorize** In the graphic organizer, list the services provided by the welfare state and the costs of those services.

Welfare State Services	Welfare State Costs

Japan Is Transformed: Text

12. **Cite Evidence** Give examples of policies Americans introduced during the occupation of Japan.

13. **Identify Cause and Effect** Why did Japan enjoy a trade surplus?

The Cold War Era

Lesson 3 Communism in East Asia

Key Terms

Mao Zedong

collectivization

Great Leap Forward

Cultural Revolution

38th parallel

Kim Il Sung

Syngman Rhee

Pusan Perimeter

demilitarized zone

Academic Vocabulary

communes: commonly owned and operated farms or communities

Lesson Objectives

1 **Analyze** how Mao Zedong turned China into a communist state.

2 **Describe** China's role in the Cold War.

3 **Explain** the causes and impact of the Korean War.

The Chinese Communist Victory: Text

1. Identify Supporting Details Why did Chinese peasants support Mao Zedong?

2. Summarize What happened to the opponents of the Communist party in China?

3. Analyze Interaction Why did Mao have to stop the Cultural Revolution?

China and the Cold War: Text

4. Analyze Word Choices What does it mean that the United States "played the China card"?

5. Compare and Contrast How was Jiang Jieshi's government in Taiwan similar to Mao Zedong's in Communist China?

The Two Koreas: Text

6. **Analyze Interactions** Based on the map of the Korean Peninsula in the fall of 1950 and other events in Asia, and remembering what was happening in the rest of Asia, what risk did UN troops take when attacking North Korea?

7. **Determine Central Ideas** How would you describe Kim Il Sung as a leader? Give specific evidence from the text.

8. **Summarize** What are some differences between North Korea and South Korea?

Interactive Reading Notepad • Lesson 3

The Cold War Era

Lesson 4 War in Southeast Asia

Key Terms

Ho Chi Minh

guerrilla

Dien Bien Phu

domino theory

Viet Cong

Tet Offensive

Khmer Rouge

Pol Pot

Academic Vocabulary

terminate: finish, bring to an end

Lesson Objectives

1 **Describe** events in Indochina after World War II.

2 **Explain** how the United States became involved in the Vietnam War.

3 **Explore** the end of the Vietnam War.

4 **Summarize** the impact of the war on Vietnam and Cambodia.

The Road to War in Southeast Asia: Text

1. **Draw Inferences** Why did the Vietnamese use guerrilla tactics against the French in Vietnam?

2. **Identify Supporting Details** Why was Ngo Dinh Diem an unpopular ruler?

The United States Enters the War: Text

3. **Identify Key Steps in a Process** What events led to the American involvement in Vietnam?

4. **Draw Inferences** How did Vietnam's landscape and geography create disadvantages for American troops?

5. **Integrate Information from Diverse Sources** Based on the map and the text, why might the United States have wanted to attack targets in Cambodia?

The Vietnam War Ends: Text

6. **Categorize** In the graphic organizer below, list the reasons U.S. leaders might have given for and against continuing the war in Vietnam.

Reasons to Continue Fighting	Reasons to Pull Out

7. **Assess an Argument** Did the domino theory end up being correct?

8. **Identifying Supporting Details** Give three reasons why the Vietnamese might have wanted to leave Vietnam after the war.

Interactive Reading Notepad

The Cold War Era

Lesson 5 The Cold War Ends

Key Terms

mujahedin

Mikhail Gorbachev

glasnost

perestroika

Lech Walesa

Solidarity

Václav Havel

Nicolae Ceausescu

Academic Vocabulary

incentive: something that encourages a person to take action or work harder

---

Lesson Objectives

1 **Understand** why the Soviet Union declined.

2 **Identify** the reforms introduced by Mikhail Gorbachev.

3 **Describe** the collapse of communism in Eastern Europe and the Soviet Union.

4 **Evaluate** how the end of the Cold War affected the remaining communist nations and the United States.

The Soviet Union Declines: Text

1. **Determine Central Ideas** In which ways did the Soviet Union not meet individuals' needs?

2. **Identify Supporting Details** How did the arms race put pressure on the Soviet economy?

3. **Cite Evidence** In the graphic organizer below, list the weaknesses of the Soviet political and economic systems.

Political Weaknesses	Economic Weaknesses

4. **Compare and Contrast** How was the Soviet war in Afghanistan similar to the Vietnam War?

167

The Soviet Union Collapses: Text

5. **Categorize** In the graphic organizer below, list the goals of glasnost and perestroika.

Glasnost Goals	Perestroika Goals

6. **Draw Inferences** Why did Gorbachev's reforms cause economic turmoil in the Soviet Union?

Eastern Europe Transformed: Text

7. **Identify Supporting Details** In what ways did Hungary lead the way to reform in Eastern Europe in 1988–89?

8. **Summarize** Explain Lech Walesa's role in the Polish people's fight against their communist government.

9. **Determine Central Ideas** Why were Eastern European reforms allowed to happen in the late 1980s? What had happened before when Eastern Europeans attempted reform?

10. **Identify Key Steps** How did the East Germans overthrow their communist leaders?

Communism Declines Around the World: Text

11. **Cite Evidence** Using the charts from the infographic, provide evidence that China's economy is becoming more capitalistic.

The Post-Cold War World: Text

12. **Cite Evidence** What kinds of roles has the United States played as the sole remaining superpower?

New Nations Emerge

Lesson 1 New Nations in South Asia and Southeast Asia

Key Terms

partition	Punjab	Sukarno
Sikh	Golden Temple	Suharto
Kashmir	Bangladesh	East Timor
Jawaharlal Nehru	nonalignment	Ferdinand Marcos
dalit	autocratic	Benigno Aquino
Indira Gandhi	Aung San Suu Kyi	Corazon Aquino

Academic Vocabulary

compelled: made to or forced

predominant: most common or numerous

Lesson Objectives

1 **Explain** how independence led to the partition of India.

2 **Describe** the national development of India, Pakistan, and Bangladesh.

3 **Define** the role of South Asia in the Cold War.

4 **Explain** the impact of independence on the nations of Southeast Asia.

Independence and Partition in South Asia: Text

1. **Identify Cause and Effect** Describe the events that led to the formation of an independent India and Pakistan.

2. **Analyze Information** Why is the conflict in Kashmir rooted in colonialism?

Challenges to Modern India: Text

3. **Summarize** Based on the text, what are some of the challenges that India has faced as the world's largest parliamentary democracy?

4. **Analyze Relationships** Why has there been a conflict between Indian traditions and some government programs since 1947?

Pakistan and Bangladesh Separate: Text

5. **Summarize** What economic and geographic factors led to the creation of an independent Bangladesh? Use evidence from the text to support your answer.

6. **Identify Supporting Details** The text states, "After independence, Pakistan struggled to build a stable government." Which details from the text support this statement?

Interactive Reading Notepad • Lesson 1

South Asia in the Cold War: Text

7. **Vocabulary: Determine Meaning** Reread the first two paragraphs under "South Asia in the Cold War." Explain what the word *colonialism* means. Why do you think the new independent nations of South Asia rejected colonialism?

8. **Identify Cause and Effect** As you read "South Asia in the Cold War," use this graphic organizer to record the causes and effects of the nonaligned movement.

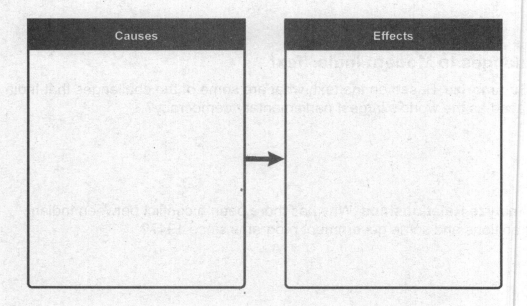

Causes	Effects

Independent Nations in Southeast Asia: Text

9. **Vocabulary: Determine Meaning** Read "Independent Nations in Southeast Asia." What do you think the word *repressive* means? What are some examples of repressive actions taken by governments in Southeast Asia?

10. **Compare and Contrast** Compare economic conditions in Malaysia to those of Myanmar. How is this difference in their economies linked to the wider differences between the two countries?

Populous Indonesia Faces Challenges: Text

11. Synthesize How has diversity posed challenges to Indonesia?

12. Cite Evidence What have been the main causes of violence in Indonesia? Cite evidence from the text to support your answer.

Struggle for Democracy in the Philippines: Text

13. Draw Inferences Why has economic growth in the Philippines been limited? Consider the factors that have been discussed in the text.

14. Compare and Contrast Choose two of the independent nations discussed in this lesson (India, Pakistan, Sri Lanka, Bangladesh, Malaysia, Myanmar, Indonesia, and the Philippines). Compare and contrast the road to independence between the two nations. What led to each nation's desire for independence, how did it gain its independence, and what effect did independence have on the growth and development of each nation?

New Nations Emerge

Lesson 2 African Nations Win Independence

Key Terms

savanna	Katanga
Kwame Nkrumah	Biafra
Jomo Kenyatta	Hutus
coup d'etat	Tutsis
Mobutu Sese Seko	Darfur
Islamist	

Academic Vocabulary

concentrated: groups of people living or working in dense numbers

export: goods sent to another country

resource: important assets

strategic: related to purposeful planning for an event

Lesson Objectives

1 **Summarize** how African nations won independence.

2 **Analyze** the issues facing new African nations and the different paths they took.

3 **Identify** examples and summarize the reasons for ethnic conflict and genocide in African nations.

The New Nations of Africa: Text

1. **Analyze Information** What role did geography play in the colonization of Africa?

2. **Summarize** Why did the European powers establish colonies in Africa? How did the establishment of these colonies affect the way independence would eventually be established?

A Variety of New Governments: Text

3. **Cite Evidence** What circumstances led to the conflicts between ethnic groups in African nations struggling for independence? Cite evidence from the text to support your answer.

4. **Draw Inferences** Why do you think the military often seized power in areas of civil unrest in Africa?

Case Studies: Five African Nations: Text

5. **Compare and Contrast** Compare and contrast the history of national independence in two of the nations in this section (Ghana, Kenya, Algeria, Democratic Republic of Congo, and Nigeria). Consider political, economic, and geographic causes, as well as conflicts among religious and ethnic groups. Also, look at where the path to independence has led for two of these nations. Fill in the chart below to organize your information.

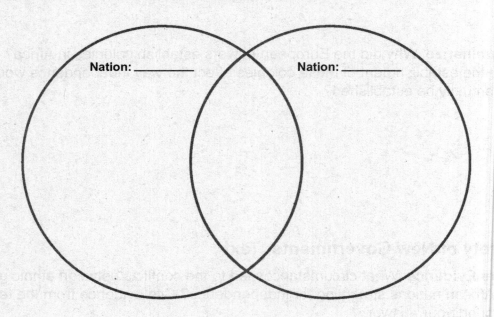

Nation: _____   Nation: _____

6. **Hypothesize** Why did the discovery of oil in Nigeria lead to greater political instability?

The Wars of Southern Africa: Text

7. **Draw Inferences** How did the Cold War affect independence in Angola and Mozambique? Why did the Cold War superpowers get involved in the political unrest in these nations?

Ethnic Conflict and Genocide: Text

8. **Determine Meaning of Words** Read "Ethnic Conflict and Genocide." What do you think the word *genocide* means? How does the situation in Rwanda contribute to your understanding of the word *genocide*?

9. **Identify Supporting Details** The text states that "Unjust governments and regional rivalries fed ethnic violence" in several African nations. Which details from the text support this statement?

New Nations Emerge

Lesson 3 The Modern Middle East Takes Shape

Key Terms

kibbutz

Golda Meir

Suez Canal

Gamal Abdel Nasser

Anwar Sadat

Ruhollah Khomeini

theocracy

secular

hejab

Academic Vocabulary

diverse: showing variety; very different

domination: complete control over someone or something

intervened: came between two events or people

Lesson Objectives

1 **Analyze** the development of modern nations in the Middle East.

2 **Describe** the founding of Israel and the impact of the Arab rejection of Israel.

3 **Understand** how oil has affected nations of the Middle East.

4 **Examine** the impact of Islam on government, law, and the lives of women.

5 **Define** the "Arab Spring."

The Challenges of Diversity: Text

1. **Vocabulary: Determine Meaning** Read "Mandates Gain Independence." What do you think the word *mandates* means? Based on this meaning, what does it mean when the text states: ". . . Britain and France were given mandates over large parts of the Middle East"?

2. **Analyze** How did the mandates after World War I contribute to tensions in the Middle East?

3. **Vocabulary: Determine Meaning** Read "Kurdish Nationalism." What do you think the word *autonomy* means? What does it mean when the text states that "Today, Kurds in Iraq have much autonomy, but many Kurds still want their own state"?

The Founding of Israel: Text

4. **Hypothesize** Read the section "Arabs and Israelis in Conflict." According to the text, "[o]ngoing efforts to end the conflict between Israelis and Palestinians have produced only limited results." Why do you think these efforts have produced only "limited results"?

5. **Understand Main Ideas** Why was the "right of return" important to the Jewish people?

New Nations in the Middle East: Text

6. Vocabulary: Use Context Clues Read the first paragraph under the heading "New Nations in the Middle East." The text contrasts countries such as Jordan and Saudi Arabia that have "hereditary monarchs" with countries like Israel and Turkey, which have multiparty systems. Based on its use in the text, what is a "hereditary monarchy"?

7. Summarize Describe the Arab Spring and its effects.

Identify Cause and Effect Using the chart below, discuss the effects of the political upheaval in Iran since 1951.

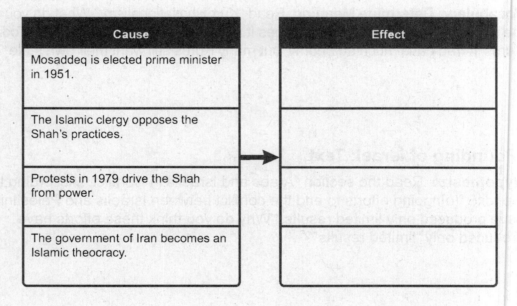

Cause	Effect
Mosaddeq is elected prime minister in 1951.	
The Islamic clergy opposes the Shah's practices.	
Protests in 1979 drive the Shah from power.	
The government of Iran becomes an Islamic theocracy.	

The Importance of Oil in the Middle East: Text

8. Infer Read "Saudi Arabia." How might the development of shale oil technology to unlock vast oil reserves in the United States affect American policy towards Saudi Arabia? Why?

9. **Draw Inferences** Read the information about the Organization of Petroleum Exporting Countries (OPEC). Based on what you've read, what is the effect of OPEC's production quotas on the global economy?

Islam and the Modern World: Text

10. **Analyze** Based on the text, what is the relationship between Islam and the various governments in the Middle East? Cite evidence from the text to support your answer.

11. **Draw Inferences** Read the quote from paragraph two of "Islam and the Lives of Women." What does this quote tell you about women in the Middle East and the Arab Spring?

"I grew up in a world where we believe we could not do anything. Generations believed we could do nothing, and now, in a matter of weeks, we know that we can."

New Nations Emerge

Lesson 4 Conflicts in the Middle East

Key Terms

Yasir Arafat

intifada

Yitzhak Rabin

Jerusalem

militia

Saddam Hussein

no-fly zone

weapon of mass destruction
 (WMD)

insurgent

Academic Vocabulary

established: set up or created

immigrated: came to live in a foreign country

radical: referring to an extreme faction of a political party

---

Lesson Objectives

1 **Explain** the ongoing Israeli-Palestinian conflict and the obstacles to peace.

2 **Explain** the causes and effects of conflicts in Lebanon and Syria.

3 **Understand** why Iraq became a battleground.

Israel and Palestine: Text

1. **Hypothesize** What is the connection between Arab defeats in wars against Israel and the use of terrorism by some Arabs?

2. **Summarize** Consider the causes and effects of the long-standing conflict between Israel and the Palestinians. Complete the chart with this information.

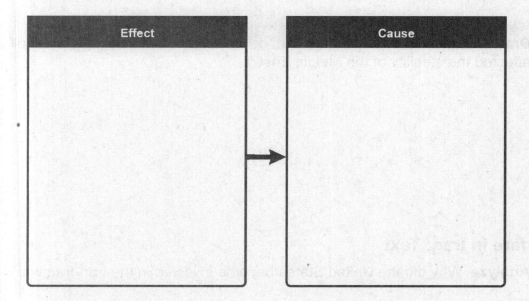

Effect	Cause

The Difficult Road to Peace: Text

3. **Summarize** What, according to the text, are the four main obstacles to peace between Israel and Palestinians?

4. **Hypothesize** Why do you think Iran and radical Islamist groups have rejected the two-state plan?

Conflict in Lebanon and Syria: Text

5. **Identify Supporting Details** What conditions led to the Lebanese Civil War? Cite supporting details from the text.

6. **Draw inferences** Based on the text, how has the extremist group Hezbollah affected the stability of the Middle East?

Warfare in Iraq: Text

7. **Analyze** Why did the United States become involved in the Iran-Iraq war?

8. **Draw Inferences** Why has the violence in Iraq continued, even after the withdrawal of United States troops in 2011?

The World Today

Lesson 1 Challenges of Development

Key Terms

development

literacy

developing world

traditional economy

Green Revolution

fundamentalist

shantytown

Academic Vocabulary

procure: make an effort to get

Lesson Objectives

1 **Understand** how nations in the developing world have tried to build strong economies.

2 **Describe** obstacles to development in the global South.

3 **Explain** how development is changing patterns of life in the developing world.

Working Toward Development: Text

1. **Identify Supporting Details** Read the first two paragraphs under "Moving Toward Modernization." Notice that the text states that "Many countries that adopted command economies suffered." What details from the text support this statement?

2. **Summarize** What were the expected consequences of the Green Revolution? What were some unintended consequences?

Challenges to Development: Text

3. **Analyze** Read the section "Populations Skyrocket." What is the relationship between population and progress in developing countries?

4. **Draw Conclusions** Have independent developing countries escaped the burdens of colonialism? Why or why not?

Interactive Reading Notepad • Lesson 1

Development Brings Social Change: Text

5. **Generate Explanations** Why do the rural poor in many developing countries move to cities? How might they be persuaded to remain in their rural homes?

6. **Identify Cause and Effect** What have been some of the effects of economic development in the developing world? Use the chart to organize your answer.

Cause	Effect
Opportunities for women have increased in developing nations.	
Families move to cities and take low-paying jobs.	
Religious revivals have swept many developing nations.	
People have flooded into cities to escape rural poverty.	

Interactive Reading Notepad • Lesson 1

The World Today

Lesson 2 Challenges for African Nations

Key Terms

apartheid

African National Congress
 (ANC)

Sharpeville

Nelson Mandela

Desmond Tutu

F.W.de Klerk

socialism

desertification

urbanization

endangered species

Wangari Maathai

sustainable development

Academic Vocabulary

stipulated: required; specified

subsidize: support with government spending

Lesson Objectives

1 **Summarize** the struggle for equality in South Africa and identify how Nelson
Mandela led resistance efforts.

2 **Describe** choices African nations had to make as they developed their economies.

3 **Understand** the challenges African nations face.

The Struggle for Equality in South Africa: Text

1. **Identify Central Issues** How did the establishment of white rule in South Africa affect the country?

2. **Identify Supporting Details** What details under "Apartheid Is Established" support the idea that "separation of the races" was designed to "keep white control over South Africa"?

3. **Identify Cause and Effect** What was the largest factor in causing F.W. de Klerk to end apartheid?

4. **Analyze Information** What role did Nelson Mandela play in changing his country?

5. **Compare and Contrast** What was life like for black South Africans during and after apartheid?

African Nations Face Economic Choices: Text

6. **Cite Evidence** What did African countries have to do in order to build productive economies? Cite evidence from the text to support your answer.

7. **Identify Cause and Effect** Why did new African nations maintain close ties to their colonial rulers? How did they benefit from a close relationship?

8. **Compare and Contrast** What were the benefits and drawbacks of socialism and capitalism for African countries?

Continuing Challenges to Development: Text

Identify Cause and Effect as you read this section. Fill in a chart like the one below with the effects of the challenges African nations still face.

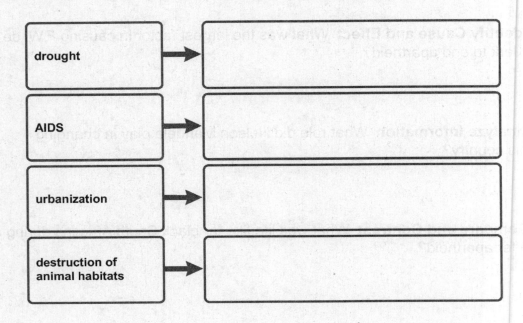

drought →

AIDS →

urbanization →

destruction of animal habitats →

9. **Integrate Information from Diverse Sources** Read the second paragraph of "Environmental Concerns." Then look at the image of Wangari Maathai. What do the text and the illustration convey about Maathai and her work? How does the image add to your understanding of the text?

The World Today

Lesson 3 Rapid Development in China and India

Key Terms

Deng Xiaoping

Tiananmen Square

one-child policy

Kolkata

Mumbai

Mother Teresa

dalit

Academic Vocabulary

disperse: break up and scatter

stimulus: something that causes something else to happen

impose: to use authority to make someone do something

Lesson Objectives

1 **Describe** how China has moved toward a free-market economy without allowing democratic reform.

2 **Identify** continuing challenges that China faces.

3 **Explain** how India has built its economy.

4 **Summarize** social reforms in modern India.

Reform and Repression in China: Text

1. **Identify Cause and Effect** How did farming change under Deng's Four Modernizations program?

2. **Identify Supporting Details** What details support the idea that urban Chinese people benefited from foreign investment?

3. **Identify Central Issues** What were students and others protesting in Tiananmen Square?

4. **Hypothesize** How do you think Chinese people responded to the massacre at Tiananmen Square? How do you think people around the world responded?

Reforms Bring Growth and Challenges: Text

5. **Identify Cause and Effect** What are some of the effects that China is dealing with as a result of rapid urbanization?

6. **Cite Evidence** How is China's economy tied to that of the rest of the world? Cite textual evidence to support your answer.

7. **Synthesize Information** Why did some people think the one-child policy was a human rights abuse? In what ways did the policy help China? Should governments worry more about individual freedoms or societal good?

Interactive Reading Notepad • Lesson 3

India Builds a Modern Economy: Text

8. **Identify Cause and Effect** Why did the Indian economy develop unevenly when it was socialist?

Identify Details As you read, use the web to record details about the challenges India faces.

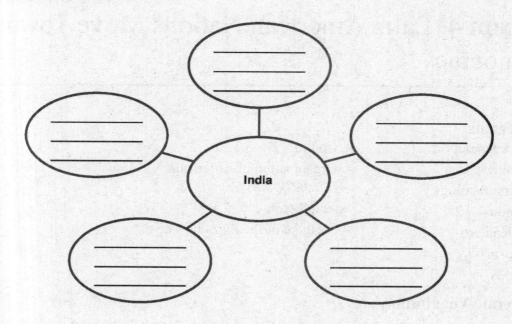

9. **Identify Central Issues** In what ways did the Green Revolution benefit India? In what way did it add to the challenge of urbanization?

10. **Summarize** Why was Mother Teresa widely admired around the world?

Social Reform in India: Text

11. **Cite Evidence** How has discrimination against women in India lessened? Use textual evidence to support your answer.

12. **Compare and Contrast** How were the steps taken to improve the lives of the dalits similar to or different from the steps taken to improve the lives of women?

The World Today

Lesson 4 Latin American Nations Move Toward Democracy

Key Terms

import substitution

agribusiness

liberation theology

indigenous

Oscar Romero

Sandinista

Contra

Organization of American
 States (OAS)

Juan Perón

Mothers of the Plaza de Mayo

Academic Vocabulary

allege: assert, charge, claim

comprise: to be made up of something

Lesson Objectives

1 **Analyze** how Latin America has grappled with poverty.

2 **Describe** the struggles of Latin American nations to build democratic governments.

3 **Explain** the struggle between repression and freedom in Argentina.

Poverty Challenges Latin America: Text

1. **Identify Cause and Effect** What impact did relying on a single cash crop have on Latin American economies?

2. **Identify Supporting Details** What details under "Promoting Industry and Agriculture" support the idea that agribusiness has negative impacts?

3. **Infer** Why have Latin American elites often resisted reforms?

4. **Identify Supporting Details**

As you are reading the section, "Population Growth Contributes to Poverty," record the main idea and supporting details on the graphic organizer below.

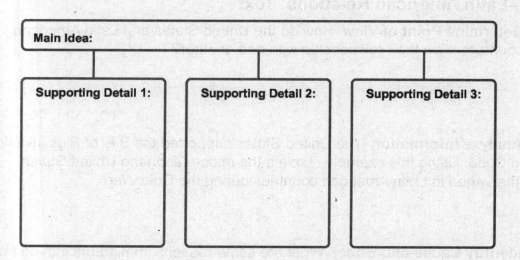

Main Idea:

Supporting Detail 1:

Supporting Detail 2:

Supporting Detail 3:

5. **Analyze Information** What effect did liberation theology have on the role of the Roman Catholic Church in Latin America?

Dictatorships and Civil War: Text

6. **Cite Evidence** Which groups in Latin America pressed for reforms starting in the 1950s? Use details from the text to support your answer.

7. **Identify Cause and Effect** What did military leaders in many Latin American nations do once they had gained power?

8. **Compare** How were the civil wars in El Salvador and Nicaragua similar? What were the goals of the parties on either side in both civil wars?

9. **Identify Cause and Effect** What major shift resulted from elections in Brazil, Venezuela, and Bolivia in the 1990s?

U.S.–Latin American Relations: Text

10. **Determine Point of View** How do the United States and Latin American countries view their relationship with one another?

11. **Analyze Information** The United States supported the Bay of Pigs invasion in Cuba. Using this example, explain the main reason the United States intervened in Latin American countries during the Cold War.

12. **Identify Cause and Effect** What are some reasons immigrants moved from Latin America to the United States? How did the economic slowdown of 2008 affect this trend?

The Long Road to Democracy in Argentina: Text

13. **Make Inferences** What can you infer from the fact that military governments were in and out of power in Argentina for several decades?

The World Today

Lesson 5 The Industrialized World

Key Terms

European Union (EU)

Euro

Northern Ireland

Good Friday Agreement

default

Vladimir Putin

surplus

deficit

Chechnya

multiethnic

Slobodan Milosevic

ethnic cleansing

Pacific Rim

Academic Vocabulary

inflation: a rise in prices linked to an increase in the amount of money available

---

Lesson Objectives

1 **Examine** social, political, and economic trends in Europe since the Cold War.

2 **Describe** how the breakup of Yugoslavia led to war and genocide.

3 **Analyze** the challenges facing Russia since the end of the Soviet Union.

4 **Summarize** economic developments in Asia.

A New Europe: Text

1. **Draw Inferences** What challenges did Germany face at the end of the Cold War?

2. **Contrast** How were the reunification efforts in Germany and Ireland different?

3. **Cite Evidence** Why is Turkey's membership in the European Union controversial? Cite evidence from the text to support your answer.

Shifts in Global Power: Text

4. **Identify Steps in a Process** What early steps in shifting to a market economy did Boris Yeltsin take? What was the effect?

5. **Summarize** How did Vladimir Putin help Russia? Why have some people criticized his leadership?

6. **Identify Cause and Effect** How did President Obama respond to the 2008 financial crisis?

The Former Soviet Republics: Text

7. **Summarize** Which areas of the former Soviet Union have experienced violent conflict?

8. **Infer** How would you characterize the relationship between Moscow and Chechnya?

War in Yugoslavia: Text

Identify Cause and Effect As you read "War in Yugoslavia," examine the text for clues that signal cause and effect. Then use a chart like this one to record major causes and effects of regions declaring independence.

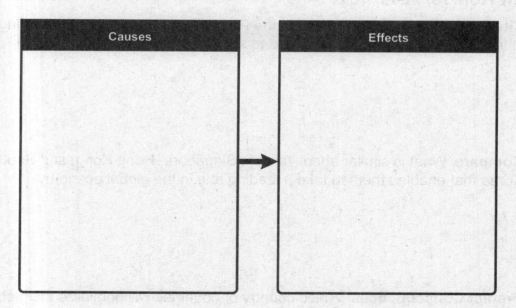

Causes	Effects

9. **Identify Central Issues** What tensions were at the root of the problems in Yugoslavia during the 1990s?

10. **Analyze Interactions** Why do you think Serbs wanted to create areas that were purely Serbian and drive people of other ethnicities away?

11. **Cite Evidence** What ethnic group was the majority of the population in Kosovo? How did this contribute to the violence there? Cite evidence from the text to support your answer.

A New Role for Asia: Text

12. **Cite Evidence** Why are nations in the Pacific well poised to take a leading role in trade? Cite evidence from the text to support your answer.

13. **Compare** What is similar about Taiwan, Singapore, Hong Kong, and South Korea that enabled them to take a leading role in the global economy?

14. **Predict Consequences** Which country or countries will dominate the global economy in the coming years? Why do you think so?

The World Today

Lesson 6 Globalization and Trade

Key Terms

globalization

interdependence

outsourcing

multinational corporation

World Trade Organization (WTO)

protectionism

bloc

sustainability

Academic Vocabulary

asset: any property that has exchange value

integrate: to combine two or more things to make one thing

Lesson Objectives

1 **Summarize** the impact of globalization on the modern world.

2 **Describe** the role of international organizations and treaties in expanding trade.

3 **Analyze** the costs and benefits of globalization.

Global Interdependence: Text

1. **Summarize** What is globalization? What are three ways countries of the world depend on one another?

2. **Identify Cause and Effect** As you read "Global Economic Crises," use this graphic organizer to record the causes and effects of the global economic downturn in the 2000s.

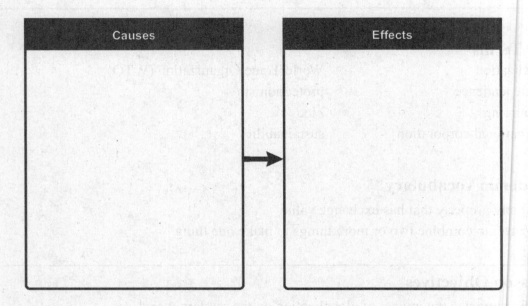

Causes	Effects

3. **Summarize** Describe the issue of debt relief in developing countries.

4. **Cite Evidence** Explain the role and significance of the United Nations. Cite evidence from the text to support your answer.

5. **Infer** How might a war or a humanitarian crisis in one country affect global trade?

Interactive Reading Notepad • Lesson 6

6. **Explain** How does the World Trade Organization work to promote international trade?

7. **Identify Supporting Details** What details under "Regional Trade Blocs" support the idea that international organizations are needed to help regulate trade?

Benefits and Costs of Globalization: Text

8. **Compare and Contrast** How do the benefits of globalization differ in developing and developed countries?

9. **Analyze** What are the costs of globalization to countries in the developing world?

10. **Hypothesize** How do you think people in the anti-globalization movement can effect change in multinational corporations?

The World Today

Lesson 7 Social and Environmental Issues

Key Terms

tsunami	acid rain
epidemic	deforestation
famine	erosion
refugee	global warming
indigenous peoples	

Academic Vocabulary

inhibit: to hold back or keep from some action

fluctuation: swing; the rising and falling of something

Lesson Objectives

1 **Explain** the impact of poverty, disasters, and disease on nations around the world.

2 **Describe** global efforts to protect human rights.

3 **Evaluate** the environmental challenges facing the world.

Global Challenges: Text

1. **Summarize** What are some of the leading causes of widespread poverty?

2. **Integrate Information from Diverse Sources** Read "Worldwide Poverty." Then look at the world map showing per capita GDP. What do the text and table convey about the status of nations around the world?

3. **Summarize** What challenges might a country face after a natural disaster?

4. **Identify Supporting Details** What details support the idea that it is difficult to contain the spread of diseases around the world?

5. **Infer** How would food distribution benefit people in war-torn countries?

6. **Identify Cause and Effect** As you read "People Search for a Better Life," use this graphic organizer to record the causes and effects of migration. What causes people to move? What are the effects?

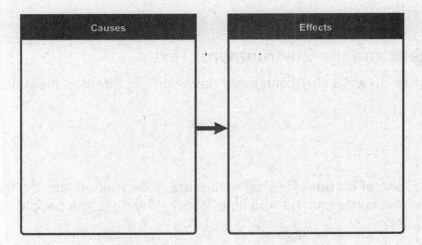

Interactive Reading Notepad • Lesson 7

Human Rights: Text

7. **Infer** Why might human rights abuses continue to occur despite the UN Universal Declaration of Human Rights and the Helsinki Accords?

8. **Cite Evidence** What information supports the idea that women around the world still suffer from unequal treatment? Use evidence from the text to support your answer.

9. **Identify Cause and Effect** Why do many children in developing nations work instead of attending school? How might this affect their future?

10. **Analyze Interactions** Why do you think indigenous peoples have often faced discrimination?

Development and the Environment: Text

11. **Summarize** In what ways can rapid development threaten the environment?

12. **Identify Central Issues** To what extent are governments around the world dealing with climate change and its effects? Why do some people oppose these efforts?

The World Today

Lesson 8 Terrorism and International Security

Key Terms

proliferate

terrorism

al Qaeda

Afghanistan

Taliban

Academic Vocabulary

priority: something deemed a priority over other things

monitor: to watch closely

acquire: to gain or come to have something

Lesson Objectives

1 **Explain** how nuclear, biological, and chemical weapons threaten national security.

2 **Analyze** the growth of terrorist groups such as al Qaeda.

3 **Explain** how the United States and other nations have responded to terrorism from September 11, 2001, to the present.

The Threat of New Weapons: Text

1. **Draw Conclusions** What is the connection between the Cold War and weapons of mass destruction?

2. **Analyze Information** How does the Nuclear Nonproliferation Treaty attempt to deal with weapons of mass destruction around the world?

Compare and Contrast As you read "The Nuclear Nonproliferation Treaty" and "Nuclear Weapons in Russia," use this graphic organizer to compare and contrast the reasons different countries have nuclear technology.

Country	Status of Nuclear Technology	Reasons
United States		
India		
Pakistan		
Israel		
Russia		
Iran		

3. **Draw Conclusions** Why are people concerned about terrorists acquiring weapons of mass destruction?

The Growing Threat of Terrorism: Text

4. **Cite Evidence** What are some tactics terrorists use to try to achieve their goals? Use evidence from the text to support your answer.

5. **Infer** Why do terrorist tactics work to draw attention to terrorists' demands and allow them to achieve small goals? How does the use of terrorism defeat an organization's goals?

6. **Identify Cause and Effect** What has been the main cause of terrorist activities in the Middle East?

7. **Summarize** What do Islamic fundamentalist groups like al Qaeda want to achieve?

The U.S. Response to Terrorism: Text

8. **Identify Cause and Effect** What actions did the United States take as a direct response to the attacks of September 11, 2001? Cite textual evidence to support your answer.

9. **Identify Central Issues** What was the reason the United States waged war against Iraq? Do you think that the war was justified?

10. **Analyze Information** How do North Korea's nuclear weapons contribute to regional instability?

The World Today

Lesson 9 Advances in Science and Technology

Key Terms

artificial satellite

International Space Station
 (ISS)

Internet

biotechnology

laser

genetics

genetic engineering

Academic Vocabulary

manipulation: the skillful handling of something with the purpose of achieving a specific result

conduct: to manage or direct something

applications: the ways things are used

Lesson Objectives

1 **Describe** the exploration of space and the innovations that have resulted.

2 **Analyze** the development and impact of computer technology and telecommunications.

3 **Summarize** key advancements in medicine and biotechnology.

Space Exploration: Text

1. **Analyze Information** Why were the contributions of Robert Goddard vital to the development of space exploration?

2. **Compare and Contrast** Compare the achievements of the United States and the USSR in space exploration during the Cold War. Identify at least one the major success of each country. How were their achievements different?

3. **Cite Evidence** What are scientists currently doing to learn more about space? Cite textual evidence to support your answer.

4. **Summarize** What are three categories of artificial satellites, and what kinds of information do we get from each?

The Computer Revolution: Text

5. **Integrate Information from Diverse Sources** Read "The Birth of Computers." Then look at the picture of early computers. What do the text and photo convey about how computers have improved since their creation?

6. **Cite Evidence** Discuss ways that computers are used in various fields. Cite textual evidence to support your answer.

7. **Identify Cause and Effect** How has the Internet shaped our world?

Breakthroughs in Medicine and Biotechnology: Text

8. Identify Cause and Effect What effect did Dr. Jonas Salk's work have on the field of medicine?

9. Infer Computers have aided doctors in diagnosing and treating diseases. What does this suggest about the role of computers in medicine in the future?

10. Compare and Contrast People have very different viewpoints regarding biotechnology. Some are in favor, and some are opposed. Use this table to record information about why people support or oppose biotechnology.

Support	Oppose
•	•
•	•
•	•

11. Summarize What have been the biggest benefits of science and technology in our world?